Integrating EMDR Into Your Practice

Liz Royle, MA, MBACP (Accredited), an experienced trauma psychotherapist, has many years' experience working with clients suffering from posttraumatic stress disorder and acute trauma reactions, including those following multiple fatality incidents, serious assaults, accidents, child sexual abuse, and major incidents. Liz is a founding member of the UK Psychological Trauma Society and leads the European Society for Traumatic Stress Studies' task force on *Managing Psychological Trauma in the Uniformed Services.* As senior welfare officer for Greater Manchester Police (GMP) up to 2004, Liz was responsible for leading a team of police welfare officers in the provision of 24-h trauma support for police officers. She was also responsible for preparing and implementing risk assessments and support procedures for vulnerable roles such as casualty bureau staff, child protection officers, and major armed crime unit. Liz has wide experience of critical incident stress management and is an approved International Critical Incident Stress Foundation (ICISF) trainer of group crisis interventions. She provided immediate and ongoing psychological support following the separate murders of three British police officers, the London bombings, and the Asian tsunami. Liz has published various papers on EMDR, including those on EMDR's use with chronic fatigue syndrome, vicarious trauma, and within the culture of the uniformed services.

Liz now works with veterans, police forces, local government, the National Health Service, and transport and security companies providing crisis interventions, psychotherapeutic support, and proactive initiatives for managing trauma. She is an accredited Europe EMDR consultant and provides training and clinical supervision to practitioners who are working with psychological trauma.

Catherine Kerr, MSc, MBACP (Senior Accredited), is a senior accredited British Association for Counselling & Psychotherapy (BACP) integrative psychotherapist, with qualifications in psychology, cognitive behavioral therapy, psychotherapy, and counseling. She was initially trained in the person-centered method of counseling, and this underpins her approach. In addition, she uses other therapeutic models and interventions as appropriate for each client. She has many years' experience of working with a wide range of people and problems and specializes in working with posttraumatic stress disorder, particularly for clients with a history of sexual abuse. Cath has completed her master's degree in psychological trauma and has worked in a variety of settings such as the private sector, community colleges, women's refuges, and the voluntary sector. She has also been in private practice and understands the different demands on therapists depending on their work setting. She is an EMDR Europe-approved practitioner; she is now working toward consultancy in this field.

Cath's experience includes the evaluation of cases, caseload management, and supervision of practitioners. Apart from trauma psychotherapy, her areas of interest and expertise include mentoring and coaching, and training and development. In addition, she has recently completed a research project exploring EMDR-trained therapists' reflections on the reasons why they have not integrated EMDR practice into their therapeutic work with traumatized clients.

Integrating EMDR Into Your Practice

**LIZ ROYLE, MA, MBACP
(Accredited)**

**CATHERINE KERR, MSc, MBACP
(Senior Accredited)**

SPRINGER PUBLISHING COMPANY
NEW YORK

Springer Publishing Company, LLC
11 West 42nd Street
New York, NY 10036
www.springerpub.com

Acquisitions Editor: Sheri W. Sussman
Production Editor: Gayle Lee
Cover Design: Steve Pisano
Composition: Ashita Shah at Newgen Imaging Systems Ltd.

ISBN: 978-0-8261-0499-1
E-book ISBN: 978-0-8261-0500-4

09 10 11 12/ 5 4 3 2 1

The author and the publisher of this Work have made every effort to use sources believed to be reliable to provide information that is accurate and compatible with the standards generally accepted at the time of publication. The author and publisher shall not be liable for any special, consequential, or exemplary damages resulting, in whole or in part, from the readers' use of, or reliance on, the information contained in this book. The publisher has no responsibility for the persistence or accuracy of URLs for external or third-party Internet Web sites referred to in this publication and does not guarantee that any content on such Web sites is, or will remain, accurate or appropriate.

Library of Congress Cataloging-in-Publication Data

Royle, Liz.
   Integrating EMDR into your practice/Liz Royle, Catherine Kerr.
      p. ; cm.
   Includes bibliographical references.
   ISBN 978-0-8261-0499-1
   1. Eye movement desensitization and reprocessing. I. Kerr, Catherine, BSc. II. Title. III. Title: Integrating eye movement desensitization reprocessing into your practice.
   [DNLM: 1. Eye Movement Desensitization Reprocessing—methods. 2. Mental Disorders—therapy. WM 425.5.D4 R891i 2010]
   RC489.E98.R69 2010
   616.85'2106—dc22   2009053401

Printed in the United States of America by Hamilton Printing.

This book is dedicated to those clients who have shared their stories with us. Their courage is inspiring and many have left footprints on our hearts.

Contents

Foreword

Thirty-five years ago, I started out as both a researcher and a "radical behaviorist" who was convinced that if I could not see it and count it then it didn't have any clinical significance. It was this same investigative process that led me to take trainings in cognitive therapy, hypnotherapy, sex therapy, gestalt therapy, group therapy, and finally in eye movement desensitization and reprocessing (EMDR). Since then, EMDR has become the major focus of my professional career as a practicing clinician as well as in my roles as research adviser and EMDR trainer.

My enthusiasm for training clinicians internationally in the EMDR approach is based primarily on the treatment effects that I have observed over the years when using EMDR clinically. Initially, these were primarily with trauma victims and those suffering from posttraumatic stress disorder (PTSD) and other trauma-related syndromes. Subsequently, it became evident that EMDR often is beneficial for patients suffering from many other types of problems as well.

As a clinician, what initially became most striking for me are the major differences in how patients resolve issues through various forms of psychotherapy. Most evident were the nuanced changes that EMDR patients made as compared to other modalities of treatment I practiced. These changes included rapid shifts in emotional reactions, shifts in perspective with regard to what had happened in the past, cognitive shifts in how patients thought about themselves and the previously distressing events in their lives as well as changes in self-esteem and a renewed sense of self. In many cases, patients resolving traumatic memories and the current symptoms with which they had long struggled made changes in ways that seemed to be almost effortless. What patients reported was that they were resolving traumatic or disturbing experiences so that these memories felt neutral and "in the past." In contrast, when using cognitive behavioral therapy (CBT) techniques, my patients had learned useful, new skills but were still managing or coping with these overwhelming events from the past. These early impressions have remained over the past two decades and I can say from personal experience that EMDR provides benefits that can offer the practicing clinician a way to provide effective, efficient, and client-centered treatment.

It is most satisfying that EMDR has garnered considerable attention from researchers over the past 21 years. Since Shapiro's seminal randomized controlled trial was published (Shapiro, 1989), more research has been reported that not only demonstrates EMDR's effectiveness in treating PTSD and other trauma-related syndromes, but also shows EMDR to be the most efficient treatment available (Bisson & Andres, 2007; Bradley et al., 2005; Davidson & Parker, 2001; Rodenberg et al., in press; Siedler & Wagner, 2006; Van Etten and Taylor, 1998). This research has corroborated those treatment effects that I have observed clinically.

Further, clinical reports suggest that EMDR is effective with a broader range of clinical issues. Reports from clinicians in many countries around the world seem to corroborate my own clinical observations that the EMDR approach may be useful with a wide range of clinical presentations including affective and anxiety disorders, somatoform disorders, alcohol and substance abuse, relational problems and attachment disorders as well as personality disorders. It also appears to be a very useful adjunct to couples and family therapies. It will be for forthcoming research to validate these additional applications.

Since the earliest published articles on EMDR, there has been some controversy. Initially, critics in the CBT community argued that EMDR "did not work." As research continued demonstrating its effectiveness, the argument morphed into "it works but it is nothing other than exposure therapy." This argument was buttressed with misinterpretations of research data or simply ignoring it entirely (Perkins & Rouanzoin, 2002; Rogers & Silver, 2002). Also, as critics have argued that the eye movements and other forms of bilateral stimulation that are integral components of EMDR treatment are unnecessary, they have ignored research specifically demonstrating the utility of eye movements themselves (Andrade, Kavanagh, & Baddeley, 1997; Christman et al., 2003; Christman, Propper, & Brown, 2006; Kavanagh et al., 2001). Further, the critics continue to ignore issues such as EMDR's greater efficiency in treatment; that EMDR is more easily tolerated as a treatment for psychological trauma by both patients and therapists alike; and lastly, that it requires minimal if any homework from patients. Regarding this latter point, exposure therapy requires hours of weekly homework by patients and if the patient does not follow through with this homework, the treatment's effectiveness is minimal.

Currently, the EMDR approach is recognized as an effective treatment for trauma by various professional organizations and governmental agencies internationally, e.g., the American Psychiatric Association (2004) and the Department of Defense and the Department of Veterans Affairs (2004) in the United States, and the National Institute for Clinical Excellence (2005) in the United Kingdom. While these determinations are based on more than 20 randomized controlled studies, of particular concern is the issue of procedural fidelity. In their meta-analysis of published treatment outcome studies, Maxfield and Hyer (2002) demonstrate that those EMDR researchers that adhered more closely to the EMDR model in their research obtained better treatment results. This underscores the importance of adherence for clinicians. The closer the therapist adheres to the EMDR procedures and protocols, the better the treatment outcomes that are obtained in clinical settings.

Over the last two decades, EMDR has evolved from a treatment method solely for PTSD and other trauma-related disorders to a comprehensive psychotherapy approach. As a psychotherapy approach, EMDR is guided by the Adaptive Information Processing (AIP) model. AIP places the central focus not on a manipulation of symptoms, such as the dysfunctional behavior, affect, or cognition, but rather on the underlying memories that are actually the source of the pathology. It is through these new lenses that the clinician is able to access the appropriate targets and assist the client in processing the disturbing memories to an adaptive resolution, and then incorporating the positive memory networks necessary for comprehensive treatment. Since a thorough understanding of this model guides the practice of EMDR, one of the key resources most useful to newly trained clinicians is the supervision/consultation process. It is not only helpful in learning the EMDR approach but also is extremely useful in assisting newly trained EMDR therapists to integrate EMDR into their established ways of conducting psychotherapy. Happily, our two authors, Liz Royle and Catherine Kerr, are seasoned psychotherapists in the United Kingdom. Not only are they well versed in providing EMDR treatment for a broad range of clinical presentations but also have years of experience providing supervision/consultation to EMDR-trained clinicians.

This book is an outgrowth of their experience during that supervisory/consultation process. The authors provide the clinician with a clear and concise clinical text with practical strategies and insights to navigate the "ins and outs" of developing their EMDR skills. The authors have organized this text so that each chapter addresses specific phases of the EMDR model and the AIP model. Chapters follow particular clinical cases and offer suggestions for what may be most effective and cautions for what to avoid. The authors offer insight into some of the basic errors and misunderstandings that new EMDR clinicians make as well as highlighting what can be helpful in making memory-reprocessing sessions go more smoothly. The goal is that newly trained EMDR clinicians can integrate EMDR conceptually and procedurally with the rest of their years of clinical experience and clinical intuition. This book is an excellent complement to formal EMDR training as well as to Shapiro's clinical text (Shapiro, 2001).

On a closing note, as I discuss EMDR with colleagues, we find that we can each integrate the EMDR/AIP model with our previous theoretical background. However, we may perceive the clinical changes differently. For example, my psychodynamically trained EMDR colleagues frequently describe "an accelerated free association" process, while CBT-trained EMDR clinicians perceive shifts in learned behavior and cognitive restructuring. But we are all considering treatment from the EMDR/AIP model, which explains not only the effects of EMDR treatment, but also the clinical phenomena observable in each of the varied orientations.

During my many years of teaching EMDR, I have observed that as therapists gain greater understanding of the AIP model and develop confidence in their EMDR skills, they find themselves relying on this approach more and more extensively in their clinical work. Further, these therapists appear to find greater satisfaction in their work and are more passionate about it. Their continued enthusiasm is a reflection of the clinical changes they observe on a daily basis with their clients.

This book will be a worthwhile resource for clinicians who are newly trained in EMDR, as well as for those with more EMDR experience who wish to improve their skills and understanding of this remarkable psychotherapeutic approach.

Gerald Puk, PhD
EMDR Europe Approved Trainer
EMDRIA Approved Trainer

REFERENCES

American Psychiatric Association. (2004). *Practice Guideline for the Treatment of Patients with Acute Stress Disorder and Posttraumatic Stress Disorder.* Arlington, VA: American Psychiatric Association Practice Guidelines.

Andrade, J., Kavanagh, D., & Baddeley, A. (1997). Eye-movements and visual imagery: A working memory approach to the treatment of post-traumatic stress disorder. *British Journal of Clinical Psychology, 36,* 209–223.

Bisson, J., & Andrew, M. (2007). Psychological treatment of post-traumatic stress disorder (PTSD). *Cochrane Database of Systematic Reviews 2007,* Issue 3. Art. No.: CD003388. DOI: 10.1002/14651858.CD003388.pub3.

Bradley, R., Greene, J., Russ, E., Dutra, L., & Westen, D. (2005). A multidimensional meta-analysis of psychotherapy for PTSD. *American Journal of Psychiatry, 162,* 214–227.

Christman, S. D., Garvey, K. J., Propper, R. E., & Phaneuf, K. A. (2003). Bilateral eye movements enhance the retrieval of episodic memories. *Neuropsychology, 17,* 221–229.

Christman, S. D., Propper, R. E., & Brown, T.J. (2006). Increased interhemispheric interaction is associated with earlier offset of childhood amnesia. *Neuropsychology, 20,* 336–345.

Davidson, P. R., & Parker, K. C. H. (2001). Eye movement desensitization and reprocessing (EMDR): A meta-analysis. *Journal of Consulting and Clinical Psychology, 69,* 305–316.

Department of Veterans Affairs and Department of Defense. (2004). *VA/DoD Clinical Practice Guideline for the Management of Post-Traumatic Stress.* Washington, D.C.

Kavanagh, D. J., Freese, S., Andrade, J., & May, J. (2001). Effects of visuospatial tasks on desensitization to emotive memories. *British Journal of Clinical Psychology, 40,* 267–280.

Maxfield, L., & Hyer, L. A. (2002). The relationship between efficacy and methodology in studies investigating EMDR treatment of PTSD. *Journal of Clinical Psychology, 58,* 23–41.

National Institute for Clinical Excellence. (2005). *Post traumatic stress disorder (PTSD): The management of adults and children in primary and secondary care.* London: NICE Guidelines.

Perkins, B. R., & Rouanzoin, C. C. (2002). A critical evaluation of current views regarding eye movement desensitization and reprocessing (EMDR): Clarifying points of confusion. *Journal of Clinical Psychology, 58,* 77–97.

Rodenburg, R., Benjamin, A., de Roos, C., Meijer, A. M., & Stams, G. J. (In press). Efficacy of EMDR in children: A meta-analysis. *Clinical Psychology Review.*

Rogers, S., & Silver, S. M. (2002). Is EMDR an exposure therapy? A review of trauma protocols. *Journal of Clinical Psychology, 58,* 43–59.

Seidler, G. H., & Wagner, F. E. (2006). Comparing the efficacy of EMDR and trauma-focused cognitive-behavioral therapy in the treatment of PTSD: a meta-analytic study. *Psychological Medicine, 36,* 1515–1522.

Shapiro, F. (1989). Efficacy of the eye movement desensitization procedure in the treatment of traumatic memories. *Journal of Traumatic Stress, 2,* 199–223.

Shapiro, F. (2001). *Eye movement desensitization and reprocessing: Basic principles, protocols and procedures* (2nd ed.). New York: Guilford Press.

Van Etten, M. L., and Taylor, S. (1998). Comparative efficacy of treatments for post-traumatic stress disorder: A meta-analysis. *Clinical Psychology & Psychotherapy, 5,* 126–144.

Preface
Stepping Up to the Plate

Don't learn the tricks of the trade—learn the trade.

—Anon

The idea for this book came through long-standing discussions between the authors about the difficulties faced by therapists fresh from an EMDR training course. As clinical supervisors of novice EMDR therapists, the authors found themselves answering the same questions and problems. A little like passing your driving test, the real learning begins once you have passed the basic training and are attempting to integrate the protocols into your existing practice.

The book is not intended to replace the authoritative text that is required reading for EMDR clinicians—Francine Shapiro's *Eye Movement Desensitization and Reprocessing: Basic Principles, Protocols, and Procedures*—neither is it a training manual. This is rather a hands-on, helpful guide based on clinical experience of the standard EMDR protocol. It encompasses the common difficulties and challenges that novice EMDR practitioners present in supervision. The book has three main aims. First, there are clear themes that arise in this early learning stage, and the book proposes to address these with a simple, understandable approach. This simplification does not, however, detract from the accuracy of the advice and guidance given. Using case examples, the book illustrates common pitfalls and strategies for preventing many of them.

Second, both authors recognize the lack of confidence that many novices talk about when they first begin. Because EMDR can be such a powerful therapy, and this is quite rightly emphasized within the training, it can discourage therapists from ever using their new skills, or can result in them giving up at the first hurdle. This can mean that clients who would benefit from EMDR are not able to access the support. Accredited

EMDR training courses are intensive and involve many participants from diverse therapeutic backgrounds. New practitioners often feel isolated. Chapters will include frequently asked questions, often the ones that were not asked during training or that have arisen since.

Third, increasing numbers of therapists are simply reading an EMDR-protocols book or seeing descriptions of EMDR on the Internet and are attempting to duplicate this highly effective therapy. As practicing EMDR therapists, the authors hear "horror stories" where EMDR has been used inappropriately or with potential to endanger clients; this is something they are passionate about rectifying. With the assumption that therapists have the right intentions, the authors considered how an "easy read" book could address these difficulties. By including "Whatever you do, don't do this," the book proposes to guide those therapists into a safer way of working while encouraging them to access accredited training and consultation for their practice. This book is not intended as a replacement for appropriate clinical supervision. Readers are encouraged to access specific EMDR consultation from a qualified practitioner.

The authors provide many case examples to illustrate key learning points. All these are either composite cases or are here with the permission of the client or supervisee. In the latter cases, identifying details have been changed. The complete eight-phase protocol is illustrated using a composite case study. This demonstrates EMDR in practice from start to finish. The standard EMDR protocol focuses on resolving distressing life events. These may be a major traumatic event such as a natural disaster or a comparatively minor trauma such as parental criticism in childhood. This book includes a number of resources drawn from other areas of therapy that can support the integration of the standard EMDR protocol into readers' practice.

The scope of the book is limited to EMDR practice with adults, taking into account practitioners' differing levels of experience and theoretical backgrounds. It is intended to cover office consultation rather than inpatient treatment. Child EMDR is a specialized area within the field of EMDR, and the authors do not attempt to address this. This is not a book about posttraumatic stress disorder (PTSD), but EMDR is one of the psychotherapeutic approaches recommended to treat PTSD. Consequently, this is where the focus of the book lies.

You may pick up this book to deal with a particular issue or read it from start to finish. EMDR is not a linear model—sometimes when things are not going to plan, we need to check our foundations, return to earlier phases, and rethink our EMDR case conceptualization. When you feel as if you are banging your head against a brick wall, it's usually wise to stop, stand back, and look at the bigger picture.

EMDR is a very powerful evidence-based therapy that can transform an individual when used with due care.

REFERENCE

Shapiro, F. (2001). *Eye movement desensitization and reprocessing: Basic principles, protocols, and procedures* (2nd ed.). New York/London: Guilford Press.

Acknowledgments

This book has been a labor of love, hard work, and dedication, and could not have been produced without the support and encouragement of some very special people.

First and foremost, we would both like to thank Dr. Francine Shapiro without whom none of us would have the opportunity to carry out this highly effective psychotherapy. This book emerged from our passion for EMDR, and we were fortunate that this was shared by Springer Publishing. A special mention goes to Sheri W. Sussman for her patience in dealing with our last-minute panics and use of the Queen's English. Our colloquialisms provided more than one challenge along the way! Dr. Gerald Puk has been a tower of strength, providing gentle encouragement, technical expertise, and wisdom. He had a strong faith in us and in the book right from the start. Over in the United Kingdom, Paul Keenan has similarly offered support, enthusiasm, and technical advice. Paul inspired Liz to continue when she was facing her own struggles to integrate EMDR into her practice and has since become a good friend and co-researcher. John Spector was a valuable link between the United Kingdom and the United States. Kath Wilkins diligently read our proofs and taught us the dangers of split infinitives. Her background in education means that we will never disrespect a comma again. Our colleague Trish Waring gave us the perspective of a newly trained EMDR practitioner, and this was important in keeping our focus on the reader.

Liz Royle: The most important people as always are my family. They have provided solid support and tolerance even when I have been grumpy and consumed with "the book." Special mentions go to my husband Gary and children Simon and Sophie for keeping me grounded. Without your support, I would not be able to do any of this. Thank you.

Catherine Kerr: To my close friends (you know who you are!) thank you for your patience and faith in me, and for always being there to support me. I would like to thank my family for their love and unwavering belief that I would finish this book, and finally, my partner Rob, who always kept me grounded and provided a constant source of wisdom, love (and home-cooked food!) when frustration and procrastination had set in.

Several clients have contributed their stories to this book. The positive outcomes they have with EMDR make it all worth it. Final thanks go to the therapists who have given permission to bring their challenges and successes to a wider community and who continued to learn and integrate EMDR into their practice even when the going got tough.

1   Who's Sitting Opposite You?

Phase 1 of the standard *eye movement desensitization and reprocessing* (EMDR) protocol is history taking. It is important to determine whether the client is appropriate for EMDR selection. Even when the presenting problem appears to be suitable for this treatment, the client may not be, and a full consideration of cautions must be made. Where EMDR is deemed suitable, the treatment plan needs to be conceptualized by taking a full history to establish the origins of the presenting problems. Many clients will have come specifically for EMDR, for others the appropriateness of EMDR as a primary treatment modality will become apparent during history taking. It can be easy to get caught up in the "technique" of EMDR and plunge straight into desensitization, but EMDR is no different from any other therapeutic approach in needing certain things to be in place before proceeding.

THE THERAPEUTIC RELATIONSHIP—BACK TO BASICS

Many practitioners who are new to EMDR suddenly lose sight of their existing therapeutic skills. This book includes reminders of some of these and provides the familiar, background context for integrating EMDR into our practice. It is important to remember that when we are learning anything new, we all go through a process, such as the conscious competence model shown in Table 1.1. Supervisees often describe finding themselves in a position of conscious incompetence regarding EMDR and, in supervision, present as disempowered, apprehensive, or downright scared to death of making a start! It may be of some comfort to know that this cautious, conscientious approach is preferable to the supervisee who rushes in and is overly confident. It cannot be overstated that EMDR is a psychotherapeutic approach and issues such as client safety, therapeutic alliance, comprehensive assessment, confidentiality, and boundary issues are paramount.

Therapists should ensure they are

- Offering the core conditions of unconditional positive regard, empathy, and congruence (Rogers, 1995; see Chapter Resource 1.1: Roger's Core Conditions)
- Creating an environment, through the development of trust and rapport, in which the client is able and willing to be vulnerable

Table 1.1   The Conscious Competence Model

Stage 1: Unconscious Incompetence
Therapists are not aware of the existence or relevance of EMDR to their practice and must become conscious of their incompetence before development of the new skill or learning can begin.

Stage 2: Conscious incompetence
Therapists become aware of the existence and relevance of EMDR and of their own deficiency in this area.
If you are reading this book then you have made the commitment to learn and practice EMDR and to move to the "conscious competence" stage!

Stage 3: Conscious competence
Therapists achieve "conscious competence" in a skill when they can perform it reliably at will. They still need to concentrate and think to perform the skill because the skill is not yet "second nature" or "automatic."

Stage 4: Unconscious competence
Therapists become so practiced in their EMDR skills that they enter the unconscious parts of the brain—it has become instinctual.
Do we ever really get there ....?

This model provides a simple explanation of the process and stages of learning a new skill. The learner or trainee always begins at stage 1, "unconscious incompetence," and moves through stages 2 and 3 to end at stage 4, "unconscious competence."

- Being flexible according to the client's needs and that they have a tool box of strategies
- Attending to client safety (see Chapter Resources 1.2: Suicide Ideation and 1.3: Brief Suicide Counseling Model).

All these are necessary before using EMDR, and many of the "failures" that are seen in supervision arise because not enough time has been spent on this foundation. They are particularly important when working with survivors of child sexual abuse and clients with posttraumatic stress disorder (PTSD). However, therapists sometimes put the above skills to one side as they focus on the protocol and their anxieties about getting that right. The practicalities of EMDR sessions should also be borne in mind. Desensitization sessions cannot be rushed, and therapists will need to allow near-double their usual session time. An early consideration therefore is whether this is feasible in the workplace setting, for example, is the therapy room being rented for 50 minutes only? Similar consideration is suggested for time-limited therapy as all the phases of the protocol need sufficient time. Dealing with more complex issues may not be possible where a client can only be seen for four to six sessions and the therapist risks "opening a can of worms" and then having to leave the client with that.

What Does the Client Need?

Clients need to be aware that the process of EMDR treatment can be disturbing and that dissociated material may surface during therapy. Because EMDR has the potential for a rapid uncovering of this unsuspected material, some of which may be extremely distressing (Shapiro, 2001), an assessment needs to be made of the client's ability to handle strong emotions. An important theme running through any theoretical work should always be client safety. Risk factors should be assessed including the following short-term high-risk factors:

- Impairment in daily functioning
- Unstable lifestyle
- Inadequate coping style and resources
- Few available significant others or reliance on one person alone
- Uncooperative in prior psychiatric treatment or unreceptive to help

- Chronic illness
- Parasuicide acts or suicides within the family
- Previous suicide attempts
- Recent losses
- Severe depression or hopelessness
- Chronic abuse of alcohol/drugs
- Unexplained improvement in clinical features.

Although highly effective, EMDR can be very hard work for clients, and both client and therapist need to be prepared to deal with whatever surfaces during therapy. Before commencing the desensitization phase, clients need to be as stable and competently resourced as possible to better buffer any deterioration in symptoms.

Clients will need varying amounts of therapy time to create this resilience. You will need to explore your client's ability to self-soothe, encourage their use of social support, and assess their control over any external stressors both current and likely to occur in the future. Other demands (such as upcoming exams, high workloads) will have an impact on the client's finite resources. Systems issues may need to be addressed, for example, the therapist working with a victim of domestic violence should consider ongoing risks.

Perhaps because EMDR has the reputation of solving problems rapidly, some clients have unrealistically positive expectations for therapy. It is important that the therapist examines these up front. EMDR is neither a panacea nor a magic wand. Where clients expect to "have something done to them" and to be passive in the process, this can have an impact

---

⊘ **Whatever You Do, Don't Do This...**

Claire came to therapy for an anxiety disorder. Her therapist introduced the concept of EMDR to her at the third session.

"Oh, I think I've had that when I saw another counselor a couple of years ago. He didn't say what it was though. It was our first meeting and I was talking about my problems when he just said 'stop there a moment,' came and sat right next to me and started waving his fingers in front of me. I don't think it really worked...."

> ⬎ *Common Pitfall*
> *The Client Is Not Ready for Therapy*
>
> On occasion, clients may have been "sent" to therapy by an employer, a well-meaning friend, relative, or a professional. Alternatively, they may have heard EMDR being described as a "quick fix" or similar and are expecting the therapist to do all the work.
>
> It is important in such cases to establish in the history-taking phase what brought them to therapy, why now, what are their hopes and expectations, and what are their fears? What do they expect to be different once they have completed therapy and what do they understand the process to be? Eliciting this information early on in the relationship can prevent frustration and disappointment and create a transparency that allows the client to make a choice as to whether to engage. It is also important to carry out regular reviews to ensure the client maintains engagement.

on their willingness to engage and utilize self-help strategies. Informative literature and directed research can help to inform clients of the true nature of EMDR therapy.

Secondary Gain

For some clients there may be ambivalence about recovery from their dysfunction or distress. This may not always be something to which they give a conscious thought, and therapists should explore the possibilities of secondary gain in a sensitive and nonjudgmental manner. Common secondary gains include the loss or reduction of a compensation claim or disability pension. Others include the loss of their identity, particularly for veterans or survivors of abuse, or for clients who identify too closely with their symptoms and struggles with life.

Dissociative Disorders

It is strongly recommended that EMDR is not used with clients who have dissociative disorders (DD) unless therapists are *confident and competent in their EMDR practice as well as in working with this client population.* Because of this, readers of this book are

> ### *Case Example*
> ### *Secondary Gain*
>
> Henry had reactive depression following serious bullying at work. During the subsequent internal investigation, he had felt unsupported by his managers and had left work to go on sickness absence due to raised levels of anxiety and disturbed sleep. An emerging secondary gain for him was that, if he recovered, he would have to return to the workplace. Additionally, he believed that he would be giving his employers the impression that he had not been that badly affected and they could forget what had happened to him—he needed to be seen to "suffer" for them to care. Recovery was equated with "forgive and forget," and he was not ready for that to happen.

advised to screen for DD and, where present, refer to appropriate professionals.

See chapter 3 for more information on DD or one of many comprehensive texts available (Dell & O'Neill, 2009; DePrince & Cromer, 2006; DePrince & Freyd, 2007; Forgash & Copeley, 2008; Karjala, 2007; Moskovitz, Schafer, & Dorahy, 2008; Ross, 1989, 1996).

Cautions

EMDR can create a physical strain on the client as high emotions and somatic symptoms are processed. Enquiries should be made about the client's general health and history of physical conditions. Table 1.2 indicates areas where caution should be exercised.

Legal Issues

There are several legal issues that concern supervisees:

- The use of EMDR during ongoing litigation cases (see Frequently Asked Questions, concluding this chapter)
- Fears that a client may sue the therapist if previously dissociated material surfaces during EMDR therapy
- Fears that a lawyer will attempt to devalue or "rubbish" EMDR or even suggest that the therapist has done harm.

Table 1.2   Cautions

CONDITION	ACTION
Contact lenses	Client may experience discomfort with eye movements and should remove contact lenses during desensitization
Eye diseases, surgery	Seek advice from ophthalmology consultant; use alternative DAS such as sound and tapping Never continue eye movements when client reports eye pain
Pregnancy	Seek physician advice and consider the appropriateness of avoiding high levels of arousal during the pregnancy
Heart condition Respiratory condition Severe physical impairment Trauma-related memories that involved severe physical sensations, for example, choking, drowning, intense pain/invasion	Seek physician advice and consider whether it is appropriate to treat as an inpatient or in a setting where medical assistance is readily accessible
Epilepsy	There is a very low probability of EMDR treatment triggering a seizure. Consult with client's neurologist as to whether increased affect or repetitive DAS would be of concern
Active drug/alcohol abuse	Consider what other support needs to be put in place. Therapists may work with such clients in partnership with professionals skilled in working with addictions. For nonactive drug/alcohol abuse, therapist and client may agree to a nonabuse contract for the duration of therapy. Clients need to be as stable as possible prior to desensitization and the risk of relapse actively monitored
Schizophrenia	Seek physician advice and assess the need for accessible medical assistance, restraint, and medication

(continued)

Table 1.2 Cautions (Continued)

CONDITION	ACTION
Organic brain damage	Seek physician advice
Prescribed medication	Medication may be needed to stabilize the client during therapy and its efficacy and appropriateness should be monitored as progress is made by a suitably qualified professional. EMDR treatment effects can be expected with most psychotropic medications except for benzodiapines because these latter medications can prevent the client from experiencing the affect and physical sensations associated with the memory he or she is working on.

If in doubt, always seek advice from an appropriately qualified physician or consultant.

Therapists are less likely to encounter scrutiny of their use of EMDR now that it has gained approval from NICE (National Institute for Clinical Excellence, 2005) for PTSD. However, the importance of gaining the client's informed consent prior to desensitization is crucial. When the therapist introduces the use of EMDR to the client, it should be made explicit that dissociated material can surface during therapy. This information should preferably be provided in written form for clients to take away. It is all too easy for clients to not absorb all the information provided to them verbally in sessions or for therapists to "forget" this part (Chapter Resource 2.3: Example Informed Consent Form) Whether therapists choose to use this type of form or simply mark that the appropriate written information was given to the client, it can provide the much needed reassurance if ever that very rare, but commonly dreaded, lawyer's letter lands on the doormat.

Pre-EMDR Questionnaire

At this point, supervisees are often wondering whether they will ever get a client who passes all the criteria for EMDR as well as feeling rather anxious about remembering to consider all of this. A useful way of checking all the boxes is to use a standard tick-list or questionnaire such as the one in Table 1.3. Therapists who are new to EMDR feel reassured that they have not missed something vital—and removing that particular worry allows them to focus on the task at hand.

Table 1.3   Pre-EMDR Questionnaire

ADDITIONAL PRE-EMDR CHECKLIST FOR ANY CAUTIONS AGAINST USING EMDR	
CHECK	**ANY COMMENTS**
Has the client got suicidal thoughts or intent? Has he/she previously attempted suicide? Has he/she reported current or previous self-harm?	
Does the client drink excessively, take drugs, gamble, or have any other comorbidity?	
What is the client's score on the Dissociative Experiences Scale? (See chapter 3 for meanings)	
Are there previous critical events in the client's history?	
Does the client know how to self-soothe? Can the client manage high affect? What coping skills are used regularly?	
Have you enhanced a safe place and does the client practice it regularly?	
If there is a current ongoing legal case, has legal advice been sought?	
Does the client have epilepsy?	
Any head injuries?	
Is the client pregnant?	
Any other medical condition? If so, does client need to see physician?	
Any medication? Prescription or otherwise	
Has client been given literature on EMDR to take away, read, and research?	
What is the client's understanding of EMDR?	
What (if any) are the client's expectations?	
What (if any) are the client's fears?	
Informed consent form signed?	
Check out preference for DAS—eye movements (EM)/ audio/tapping	First choice: Second choice:
If using eye movements, does the client wear contact lenses/glasses? Has the client got any eye diseases or problems with his or her eyes other than refractory problems?	

CASE STUDY: INTRODUCING EMMA

Throughout this book, we will be illustrating common pitfalls as well as offering techniques and advice on how to avoid them. A variety of case examples will be shown in text boxes but we will also be taking readers through a complete case from start to finish. Emma's is a composite case study, and information relating to her case will be described in text boxes so that readers can more easily follow her progress. A snapshot of Emma's assessment below gives a rough guide as to the kind of information that should be gathered to determine suitability for EMDR.

CASE STUDY: EMMA

Emma was 27 years old; she was of medium build with dark brown shoulder-length hair. Quietly spoken and very nervous on our first meeting, she could hardly look at me and her shoulders were bent forward as she sat on the edge of the seat. Emma was dressed in a grey shapeless jumper and baggy jeans that appeared to swamp her. She took a while to tell me that she had decided to seek therapy following a "bad experience with a boyfriend." She began by telling me how stupid she was being and that she should not have got herself in this situation. She was clearly embarrassed about telling her story and needed reassurance that she would not be judged. It transpired that, 6 months ago, she had been out for the night with a new boyfriend, Duncan. She had seen him a couple of times previously and was enjoying his company. At the end of the night, they had shared a taxi home and she had invited him into her shared apartment for a coffee.

"I suppose I gave him the wrong impression. We were having a lovely evening talking and laughing, and I just wanted it to carry on a little longer."

Emma became increasingly tearful as the story unfolded, and she expressed anger with herself. I just let her talk, focusing on providing a safe relationship for her to do so.

Duncan had followed Emma into the kitchen, and although she had initially welcomed his advances, he became more insistent and had eventually forced her to have sex. Emma was devastated and blamed herself.

"He kept telling me I'd led him on, how he'd spent a fortune on a fancy restaurant, and now I was being selfish. He said I shouldn't wear what I was wearing if I didn't want sex. It was just a pretty summer dress—I've thrown it away now. Afterward he kissed me goodbye like nothing had ever happened. I must have missed all the warning signs. I thought he was a nice guy. Maybe it is my fault ...."

Emma was having difficulty with her reaction to what had happened. She explained that since it happened, she had become very withdrawn, would not venture out at night, had mood swings, and had lost her "sense of self." She had also started to have panic attacks and was blaming herself for what had happened, so she had not reported it to the police.

"They're not going to take it seriously. Let's face it, they'll just think I was stupid asking a man back when I'd had a few drinks. It'll be my word against his and it probably was my fault. I just want to be able to put this behind me and move on."

She was now complaining of poor concentration and being unable to sleep, and she spent most of her time at her mother's home, not getting dressed all day as she was currently on sickness absence from work.

EMMA'S CASE SHEET

Name and reference number:
Emma Smith—07/ST

Address:
Currently resides at mother's home
123 Rainbow Walk
San Francisco, CA
94111
Telephone No: (915) 555-5555

Occupation:
Human Resources Manager

Contract signed: Yes
Emergency contact—relationship, name, and telephone number:
Mrs. Smith (mother)—as above

Family and significant others:
Parents: mother, Carol, 59 and father, Martin, 60 (lives 23 miles away)
Both of good health and supportive but father unaware of situation
Mother single; father remarried, no children with new wife Wendy
Brother, James, 34, lives 120 miles away and "busy with his family but we speak often." Good relationship with his daughters, Maisie, 6 and Chloe, 10
Parents divorced 19 years ago
Grandmother, Vera, 83, in nursing home
Good friends, Kate, Susan, and Charlotte (unaware of whole story; Emma has isolated herself).

Psychological well-being prior to the incident (including suicide ideation, alcohol/drug usage, previous counseling):
Good social network, lived happily and independently in an apartment. Works hard.
No previous mental health issues. Social drinking only—none at all since incident.
No previous suicide ideation or intention.
Previously healthy diet and regular exercise. Hobbies included music, holidaying, and dancing.

Previous critical incidents or significant life events:
See lifeline

Postincident history and summary of current situation—last seen GP/medication?
Impact of Events-Revised Scale (Weiss & Marmar, 1996) completed: Yes
Scores: avoidance = 16; intrusion = 21; hyperarousal = 24

Other information:
Emma had been to her physician 1 week ago and had been offered antidepressant medication, which she declined. Now just seeing GP for sickness absence certificates.

Psychoeducation literature and explanation	Given
Leaflet on understanding trauma reactions	Session 1
The body's arousal system, the panic diagram, and dealing with hyperarousal	Session 1
Self-nurturing activities leaflet	Session 2
Fact sheet 1—Managing sleep disturbance	Session 1
Fact sheet 2—Managing symptoms of reexperiencing	Session 2
Fact sheet 3—Managing symptoms of avoidance and numbing	Session 2

Arrangements made with client:
Initial weekly contract for 10 sessions followed by review

Initial reflections:
Emma has good resources but needs to be encouraged to use them. She seemed committed to following the advice given regarding symptom management.
Systems control is reasonable. Her employers are not putting any pressure on her to resume work. However, this may change.
Themes from lifeline and assessment reflect safety, shame, being deserving, and blame (highlighted in bold).
Emma seems to have a need to work hard (school and employment), and I wonder what is driving this?
Does she have suppressed memories around divorce?

IS EMDR SUITABLE FOR THE CLIENT?

It can be tempting for therapists, particularly when they are fresh from basic training and keen to use EMDR, to want to practice desensitization skills at any available opportunity. However, time properly spent on history taking and preparation will pay dividends when they do begin desensitization. It really is a case of "More Haste, Less Speed."

During history taking, the therapist needs to consider carefully any early memories that may be responsible for setting the groundwork for the current dysfunction, in addition to the present complaints and goals for the future. From the moment the client enters the consulting room, therapists can be listening attentively for negative self-evaluations and paying attention to the client's unspoken communications. Sometimes stabilization work may be needed before getting a detailed history, particularly with more traumatized clients.

Impact of the Past

Because past events can often be responsible for current dysfunction, careful exploration needs to be made of the client's history. It is equally important to be aware of the past because of the potential for these events to surface during desensitization. Never assume face validity. There is a variety of methods for exploring additional past occurrences, and therapists should be flexible in their approach. It is important never to assume anything about the clients' presenting issues, therefore, whatever the therapist's theoretical orientation, a structured in-depth assessment and/ or detailed exploration of history and symptomatology is advised. Some clients will find it more difficult to provide a full history to the therapist. Reasons for this can include shame, feelings of overwhelm when they focus on all the negative events in their past, and difficulties articulating or organizing their thoughts.

The Top Ten

Clients can be asked for the "top 10 significant events in their life." It can be revealing to have the client include good and bad events in this. Some clients will struggle to come up with 10 events and may be better asked "what have been the worst/most challenging things you have experienced/witnessed in your life?"

⊘ *Whatever You Do, Don't Do This...*

Peter came to therapy because he had been experiencing distressing nightmares in which he was horrifically attacked by a stranger wielding a machete. The nightmares had started around 2 years ago but were increasing in intensity and having a major impact on his waking day. He had become anxious and hypervigilant and was confused as to why he was suffering in this way.

Peter revealed no trigger for the onset of the nightmares. He was a social worker, and he enjoyed his work and had a settled home life. In fact, this was his motivation to sort out his problem as he was concerned that if he continued this downward spiral, then he could lose this.

The EMDR practitioner who saw Peter asked why he had chosen EMDR specifically as a treatment method.

"Oh, my neighbor is a therapist and she had been on an EMDR course. We were at a party and she offered to cure my spider phobia. It worked a bit..."

And when was that...?

"Ooh, around 2 years ago..."

Sure enough, detailed history-taking sessions revealed that his neighbor's "party trick" had uncovered traumatic material from his early childhood that, fortunately once reprocessed with EMDR, led to the cessation of his nightmares and their resulting effects.

Creative Exploration

Clients and therapists may be more comfortable with creative exploratory exercises such as creating a lifeline. Using paper and pen, the client is encouraged to "plot" his or her lifeline. Starting at birth and ending with the present day, the client will mark significant markers along the way.

A similar exercise asks clients to depict their life on paper, as a corridor with doors on either side. Behind the doors are significant events and memories. The client does not need to open the door at this stage but can give each door a label. This serves to highlight to the therapist

⬎ *Common Pitfall*
The Client Talks Too Much or Too Little

One of the common complaints from supervisees is that "it's like pulling teeth!" Some clients find it very hard to actually be in therapy and open up to a complete stranger. Some lack the ability to articulate their emotions or experiences. With many traumatic events there is an element of shame or fear of being judged.

It's strange that, fresh from training, supervisees often forget or dismiss how they would usually handle this in their practice and get caught up in EMDR being somehow different. This is particularly common where the client has come specifically for EMDR and just wants to get on with the desensitization! If the groundwork, in terms of relationship building and history taking, is rushed, then there is a much greater probability that problems will surface later on. Being consciously incompetent, it is very easy to give in to the pressure to do this and ignore your therapeutic instinct and experience.

Always ensure that the client is able to be open and vulnerable with you *before* tackling traumatic material in desensitization. Otherwise you will probably find that they somehow block their processing and you will both feel like failures.

Conversely, supervisees often bring the concern that the client is talking too much during the history taking, going off on tangents and overwhelming the therapist with fine detail. Things to remember here are:

- This may be the first time that the client has ever been listened to—never underestimate the power of letting clients tell their various stories

- Visual techniques such as lifelines and spider diagrams can be helpful to allow the client to focus

- While clients are talking, they are offering up clues to the therapist about how they view themselves and others. For example, Harry could be awarded a gold medal for talking and the therapist was anxious to focus on the protocol. However, during this time Harry was feeling "heard" for the first time ever, thus building trust and rapport. His conversation was regularly dotted with phrases such as "they changed the goalposts," "I never get what I need," and "I'm on a treadmill." Picking up on these themes helped later with the thorny subject of identifying negative cognitions.

(continued)

> ### ☙ *Common Pitfall*
> ### *The Client Talks Too Much Or Too Little (continued)*
>
> ■ Where the "verbal torrent" appears to be a defense mechanism, pushing the therapist away, this needs to be gently challenged.
>
> In both the above cases, think "If I hadn't done my EMDR training, how would I handle this?"

the existence of an event while keeping the client safe from its content until such time as sufficient trust and resources are present.

Maureen Kitchur's Strategic Development Model for EMDR (Shapiro, 2005) builds on genogram mapping formats to explore key events, family systems, and dynamics.

An example of a mapping exercise is shown below for Emma.

CASE STUDY: EMMA'S LIFELINE

AGE	EVENT	CLIENT'S COMMENTS
0–5	Happy childhood	We lived in a nice town and I've got lots of happy memories, stuff like picnics and having friends round to the house.
5–11	Loved school, "my haven"	My teacher, Mrs. Jones, was really kind, and I remember she always used to put my artwork up on the wall. I think my parents were going through a bit of a hard time then so **school was my haven.** I always looked forward to it. **I don't remember any friction at home, but my brother James tells me there was a lot.**
9	Parents divorced Went to stay with aunt for a while with two older cousins	I don't remember much about the divorce other than that **my mum lost her temper with me** and James once. It must have been hard for her, and **we were probably being a nuisance.**

(continued)

AGE	EVENT	CLIENT'S COMMENTS
11	Friend of her cousin molests her during summer holiday	He was a lot older I think—about 17—he grabbed me and touched my breasts. I was an early developer, and **I was ashamed and scared**. My cousin came in the room, and I ran back to my aunt's house. **My aunt went mad** when I told her. She said **I shouldn't have been** hanging around with the older boys.
11	Moved to new area and starts secondary school	We moved to the town where we live now, and I started a new school. **I didn't really like it much, being the new girl, and it was very different from my old school.** I **worked hard** though and did well.
11–16	Settling into new school	**I was the quiet one**, but I got a good circle of friends and didn't have any problems with bullying or anything like that.
18–21	Went to college studying	I loved college. I felt **grown up at last** and I enjoyed my course.
21– to date	Got taken on by current employer	**I was lucky** to get the job. I think they decided to take a chance on me.
25	Promoted	**I've been very lucky.**
26	Minor road traffic accident	Just **glad it wasn't my fault** and no one was hurt
27	Index event	

Assessment Tools

There are various diagnostic tools that have been devised to identify PTSD as defined in *DSM IV* (American Psychiatric Association, 1994), including the Structured Clinical Interview for *DSM-IV-PTSD* (First, Spitzer, Gibbon, & Williams, 1997). In addition, there are a range of psychometric tests that determine the level of severity once the diagnosis has been made, such as the PTSD Symptom Scale and the Clinician-

> ☛ **Common Pitfall**
> *Clients Are Overwhelmed by Negative Experiences and Unable to Find Anything Positive About Their Lives*
>
> Occasionally clients can present in therapy with such an overwhelming history of negative events that it can be difficult to draw on anything positive that has happened in their lives. In such cases, it is important during the first phase to be aware and to focus and highlight the clients strengths and resources, what they put in place to survive these events, how the events ended (did their actions contribute to this?), and whether they protected other people. Emphasize the courage it takes to come to therapy and face their fears. Check out how they might view someone else who had come through similar experiences and was, for example, holding down a job, raising a family, and living day to day.

Administered PTSD Scale (Blake et al., 1995). Also, the Impact of Events Scale—Revised (Weiss & Marmar, 1996) is the primary psychological test to identify a client's reactions to a specific traumatic event.

These tests can be helpful in determining various features of post-traumatic stress and can also have the added advantage of validating a client's symptoms. However, if clients are ill-prepared prior to completing the appropriate questionnaires, they can be left feeling more helpless and/or hopeless. It is important therefore to be sensitive to preparation for, and timing of, the test as well as to normalize the client's current experiencing of reactions. Some of the questions may be open to different interpretations by both the client and the therapist, and, depending on the levels of trust and rapport, the client may not be ready to be totally honest with the therapist. Conversely, some clients may find it easier to disclose a past traumatic event in writing rather than verbally. Flexibility is the key.

Because the effects of a traumatic incident can be wide ranging, it can be argued that some tests can be deficient and may omit certain idiosyncrasies. Thus, an individual may fall "under the radar" of the diagnostic tests by not falling neatly into the DSM IV diagnostic categories. As such Briere and Spinazzola (2005) suggest the concept of "multidimensional spectrum level phenomenon" to prevent oversimplification. Blanchard and Hickling (as cited by Scott & Stradling, 2001) highlight that, to meet the DSM IV criteria for PTSD, the individual must meet a certain number and type of criteria. However, because the client who does not quite meet those measures is unlikely to be clinically different, they propose the idea of a "subsyndromal" level of trauma, which still warrants therapeutic intervention.

There is a danger that by using one trauma-specific diagnostic tool, other diagnoses could be overlooked. It is important that such tools are not used in isolation but rather used as part of a comprehensive approach.

Presenting Problems

It may seem obvious to state that the therapist needs to know what has brought the client to therapy, yet occasionally supervisees will neglect to spend sufficient time on this clarification as they focus on the event(s) that is "crying out" for desensitization.

Clients may describe their problems in a variety of ways including their symptoms of distress, dysfunctional behaviors, negative emotions, or feeling held back from a fulfilled life. The therapist needs to explore with the client the latter's perception of the initial cause and duration of symptoms along with the frequency and intensity. Current triggers for distress should be identified. It is important to ask about other complaints that the client may or may not feel to be related so as to ensure as complete an understanding as possible of the whole picture (Chapter Resources 1.5: Mapping Exercise and 1.6: Identifying Symptomatology Using the Film Script).

At this point, it may be appropriate to offer psychoeducation and normalization of symptoms, and this in itself can prove of great relief to a client.

Goals for the Future

It is important to elicit the client's desired future state and goals for therapy. A simple question such as "If you had a magic wand and you could use it to change your life tonight, how would you know this had happened when you woke up the next day?" Although this may seem obvious, in cases of bereavement the therapist may need to acknowledge the reality that the person who died cannot come back before asking the question.

Defining goals using the SMART acronym below helps to focus the client and inspires thoughts of the possibility of a different life.

For example, the client who states "I just want to be happy ..."

Case Example
Symptom Clarification

Jane complained of not sleeping very well. The therapist explored this with her.

Therapist: So could you perhaps describe a typical night, in terms of what time you go to bed, how long it takes to get to sleep...

Jane: Well, I generally go to bed around 10:30 P.M., but it takes me a couple of hours to get to sleep.

Therapist: What's happening in those 2 hours?

Jane: I tend to toss and turn, I'm very fidgety and my mind then starts obsessing about things.

Therapist: Like?

Jane: Well, it can be things that happened during the day, or thinking about (the incident), worrying about what I've got to do next week.

Therapist: How much time is thinking about general worries and how much about (the incident)?

Jane: I suppose about 60% general stuff and 40% (the incident). It tends to be a spiral—I start worrying about the day-to-day stuff and move on to the incident.

Therapist: And then what happens?

Jane: Well, sometimes I get up and make a cup of coffee and other times I'm just so tired I eventually fall asleep.

Therapist: And what happens next?

Jane: Most nights I have bad dreams where I'm being chased or some-one's in the house. Usually this wakes me up, and I have to get up and put the lights on.

Therapist: How often?

Jane: Well, this week I've had dreams every night, last night was bad because I knew we had this session... I'd say I get up four nights out of the week.

(continued)

Case Example
Symptom Clarification (continued)

Therapist: When you do get up, what do you do after you've put the lights on?

Jane: Usually read some of my books or watch TV until I've calmed down. Quite often I can fall asleep when it starts getting light outside. Then I sleep in until about 10 A.M., if I can.

Therapist: Does this have an impact on your daily functioning?

Jane: Oh yes! I've got in trouble at work for being late or I'm bad tempered all day because I'm tired and then I feel bad. Sometimes I get on the couch for an hour when I get home and just have a cat nap.

Therapist: What time is that generally?

Jane: About 5 P.M. I only work short days thank goodness, 11 A.M. until 4:30, otherwise I don't know how I'd cope.

Therapist: Can you tell me a bit about your bedtime routine? What time do you eat your evening meal?

Jane: About 8 P.M. I go to the gym most nights as I've heard that exercise helps so I eat quite late. Then I watch TV and have a hot bath around 10 before I go to bed with my book.

Therapist: What do you have to drink in the evening?

Jane: I have to admit to a couple of glasses of wine—they help me sleep, but I have a pint of water before my bath so I'm not dehydrated. I'm really trying to do the right things...

Following this clarification, primary therapeutic goals included teaching the client basic sleep hygiene and techniques for managing nightmares. Without clarifying the symptom, these may have been missed as necessary. Jane was trying hard to do the right things but unfortunately many of her efforts were counterproductive. Providing psychoeducation gave her choices and empowered her to make positive changes that would underpin her further treatment.

Specific

What does happy mean to you? What are happy people like? Whom do you know who are happy (role model)?

Measurable

What would be different if you were happy? What would you see, do, feel? Who would be the first to notice and what would they see differently?

Achievable

Avoid goals where happiness depends on external influences that are out of the client's control or dependent on other's reactions, for example, if my parent no longer criticized me. Equally, the goal of being a 75-year-old ballerina may need some gentle challenging.

Realistic

Requests to win the lottery or to be happy 100% for the rest of their lives are perhaps not realistic.

Time Framed

This will give an indication of the client's willingness to participate actively in the therapy, offer a reality check, and inspire hope.

Although this can be an empowering process for most clients, some may find it hard to imagine things being improved ever. A balance is needed between inspiring hope for recovery and making false promises. As with any other psychotherapeutic approach, goals should be set collaboratively and neither too low nor too high.

Particularly in cases of complex trauma, it is helpful to review these goals regularly as they may change as the client does.

Treatment Plan

By this stage, the therapist should have as complete a picture as possible and, only when this is done is it possible to begin conceptualizing the treatment plan.

The treatment plan identifies specific targets for reprocessing. These include the past memories that appeared to have set the pathology in process, the present situations that exacerbate this dysfunction, and the desired future response. Where clients have identified groups of memories with parallel cues (e.g. similar negative cognitions, emotional or physical reactions) these may be clustered to maximize the generalization effect.

This can be a complex area, yet is fundamental to the effectiveness of EMDR, later chapters elaborate on treatment planning.

FREQUENTLY ASKED QUESTIONS

Q: **My client is a police officer involved with a major court case in which he is to be called as a witness to a serious assault on a child. Because he wasn't the victim, is it okay to use EMDR around his intrusive images of the incident?**

A: Providing EMDR may be construed as rehearsing the client or changing his perception of the incident therefore calling into question his evidence. It may also fade his images of the event and have an impact on his ability to recall vital detail of those images. This could have serious consequences for his testimony and the victim. For any client involved in litigation, advice on using EMDR should be sought. Clients may still wish to proceed but you should ensure they are giving informed consent (Chapter Resource 2.3).

Q: **My client only wants to deal with a later trauma but she was abused as a child. She says she's dealt with that. Is it OK to proceed?**

A: This raises several questions. Firstly, there is no way of preventing dissociated or unresolved material from surfacing during desensitization. For this reason, the client needs to be fully informed that her earlier abuse may come up. Additionally, it may be helpful to gently challenge the client about any reluctance to discuss all past trauma. This could indicate that the therapeutic relationship needs strengthening or that the client is using avoidance techniques. Finally, links to earlier trauma may not always be apparent but it may not be possible to fully address later trauma if its foundation lies in these earlier issues.

Q: **Do I need to take a full history for every client? One of my clients has come for EMDR for a phobia and doesn't wish to discuss her past.**

A: Yes. In the authors' opinion, this is probably the most important phase and is the foundation for later work. Get this wrong and you will most certainly encounter problems later. This also avoids a "fishing expedition" and allows the client some control and understanding of his or her current reactions. Using a gardening metaphor, it is helpful to explain to the client that the presenting problem is rather like an insidious weed. The roots need to be completely removed in order to prevent its return. It is strongly urged that the therapist does not assume that the presenting problem, for example flying phobia, has only face validity. The memory network may contain other earlier experiences besides those involving flying, possibly associations to feeling out of control or unsafe.

Q: **How do we know if we've got all the information from the history taking? I'm worried that my client may not disclose something relevant or may not even be aware of dissociated material.**

A: It is important to explain the rationale for taking the client's history so that the client can take responsibility for what he or she discloses. At some point we have to trust that the clients are doing this and we have given them sufficient opportunity to build a safe relationship in which he/she can do this. However, some memories may be preverbal or dissociated. The therapist needs to remain alert to new material and have ensured that the client is fully prepared for this eventuality. The informed consent form will help with this awareness, but the preparation phase is crucial. As we know from experience, many clients will identify additional memories as treatment progresses.

Q: **Is EMDR going to work with conditions other than PTSD?**

A: EMDR was originally developed to treat traumatic memories and its efficacy for PTSD is well documented (Chemtob, Tolin, van der Kolk, & Pitman, 2000; Clinical Outcomes Efficiency Support Team [CREST], 2003; Department of Veterans Affairs & Department of Defense, 2004) with many randomized studies supporting its efficacy (Carlson et al., 1998; Ironson, Freund, Stauss, & Williams, 2002; Power et al., 2002; Soberman, Greenwald, & Rule, 2002). EMDR has also been reported as being effective in the treatment of other psychological problems, for example, Body Dysmorphic Disorder (Brown, McGoldrick, & Buchanan, 1997), Non-Psychotic Morbid Jealousy (Keenan & Farrell, 2000), Phantom Limb Pain (Tinker & Wilson, 2005), Vicarious Trauma (Keenan & Royle, 2008), Anxiety Disorders (Shapiro, 2005), and Chronic Fatigue Syndrome (Royle, 2008). EMDR is not, however, a panacea, and no psychotherapeutic approach is 100% successful.

Some of the indications that EMDR may be an effective therapy include:

- Intrusive imagery or other "stuck" sensory material such as smells or sounds

- Repetitive dreams and nightmares
- Where the client rationally knows that something is untrue (e.g., I'm safe) but emotionally/behaviorally disagrees with this
- A strong negative self-evaluation that is unjustified
- Unexplained somatic symptoms

It is equally important to be aware of the appropriateness of education, marital therapy, assertiveness, anger management training, and problem solving when a client enters therapy.

LEARNING SUMMARY

You should feel confident that you are able to:

- Begin to build the therapeutic relationship
- Assess whether the client is ready for therapy and, in particular, to consider the following:
  - A risk assessment of client safety
  - Any potential secondary gain issues
  - Screening for DD (see chapter 2)
  - Any physical contraindications
  - Legal issues
  - Client's ability to self-soothe and access social support
  - The existence (or likelihood) of external stressors and their potential to have a negative impact on the client
- Take a full history from the client including:
  - Past events that may be unresolved or contributing to the current presenting problems
  - Present dysfunction
  - Their goals for the future.

RESOURCES

1.1: Carl Roger's Core Conditions

Carl Rogers (1995) said that there are three core conditions: respect (also known as unconditional positive regard), genuineness, and empathy. He suggested that the three conditions are "core" because they are necessary for development to take place.

Respect is about valuing the other person as a human being. This does not involve approving of all of the other person's behavior, but appreciating the other as a person. Each person is unique, and therefore has something to contribute to the experiences of others. Whether this contribution is regarded as positive or negative, it stems from the values of the perceiver. Being nonjudgmental is an important characteristic of therapy. Although the therapist will have his or her own values, it is not part of therapy to make judgments about the client. Acceptance is another term that is sometimes used for this core condition.

Genuineness is a characteristic of the therapist in the relationship. Rogers said that he aims to be "transparent" in this relationship. In other words, there is nothing that he is feeling or thinking that he wished to hide from the client. If, for example, there is some aspect of the client's behavior that Rogers finds difficult or disagreeable, then he would aim to find a way to share this with the client. It is arguable that if these perceptions are not shared, then they will still be present and influence the therapist's behavior in his or her relationship with the client. Openness is preferable, and in the long run, more therapeutic for the client.

Empathy is a characteristic that the therapist brings to the relationship. It involves being able to perceive a situation as the client perceives it. This is sometimes referred to as being within the client's "frame of reference." The therapist is able to see things as the client does. It is very different from sympathy. Sympathy is concerned with appreciating how someone else feels because that is the way you would feel in that situation. Because we are unique, this cannot precisely be the case; we can only approximately know how someone else feels in or about a particular situation. Often we may think that we know, but fall wide of the mark.

1.2: Suicide Ideation and Intent

It is not true that most people who complete suicide do not tell anyone. Eighty percent of the people who kill themselves have communicated their intention. Probably the biggest indicator of suicide is hopelessness. Other indicators can include stating goodbyes and putting affairs in order. The suicidal person's ambivalence can lead to vague references to suicide and an expectation that the helper will inevitably understand these communications.

Therapists should always explore throwaway comments such as "I've had enough, they'd be better off without me, I can't stand this."

It is not true that if you mention it you may put the idea into his mind. If the idea isn't there you will get told that he has no intention of doing that. If it is there, he will feel able to be more open about thoughts that he may have felt ashamed to admit. The opportunity to discuss suicidal thoughts can give relief and enable a person to put thought between impulse and action. The greater risk is that the idea becomes shameful and increases a sense of low worth and isolation.

It is not true that people who make suicidal gestures never do kill themselves. Some of them do kill themselves. Even if they may have half-hoped that they would be found, if they are very unlucky they still end up dead.

If the means of completing suicide are removed, then suicide rates will drop. As more cars are fitted with catalytic converters, asphyxiations by car fumes will drop. The suicide rate dropped significantly in the 1960s when British homes switched to natural gas. A government initiative in the 1990s made buying large quantities of paracetamol more difficult in an attempt to reduce overdoses. Where there is suicide ideation, the therapist should explore the extent of plans to carry this out.

	LOW RISK	MODERATE RISK	HIGH RISK
Method	Undecided	Decided	Decided
Availability of method	No	Yes	Yes
Time and place	Not specific	Not specific	Specific
Lethality	Low	Moderate	High
Final arrangements	None	Some planning	Written notes, wills, possessions given away

It is untrue that people who really want to die will find a way or that it would not help to try and stop them. The impulse to commit suicide is generally an acute, transient experience that often passes if delayed. Most suicidal people are highly ambivalent about suicide—often simultaneously desiring death, while desperately wishing to be rescued.

It is not true that if someone survives a suicide attempt it must have been a manipulative act. People usually have complex reasons for attempting suicide, and manipulation by itself is usually insufficient reason.

1.3: Brief Suicide Counseling Process

Recognize the risk

> Listen actively
>
> Look out for hints and desperate words
>
> Look at the whole person; body language, demeanor, self-care

Explore the risk

> Important to maintain Roger's Core Conditions
>
> Use explicit language
>
> Accept depth of feelings. The current crisis may be caused by something that seems almost trivial, but in reality this may be the final straw, often a culmination of events.

Assess the level of risk

> Assess short-term and historical risk factors

Interrupt the process

> Gently challenge cognitive distortions
>
> Instill hope
>
> Build relationship
>
> Delay action on impulses
>
> Help with problem solving
>
> Establish reasons for living/not dying
>
> Mobilize internal resources

Close session

> Mobilize external resources
>
> Refer on
>
> Help with time structuring and contract setting

Look After Yourself

Self-care and supervision: Take a few minutes after dealing with the situation to calm down. It is very normal to feel anxious, sad, or "fired up" after this kind of intervention. If you can, get some fresh air, speak to a colleague or your supervisor, have a cup of tea, or move away from the environment you were in. Do not throw yourself headlong into another intensive piece of work until you feel calmer.

Consider self-use of EMDR, that is, using sets of dual attention stimulus (DAS) to reprocess your reaction to this emotionally intense session. See Shapiro (2001) or your EMDR Part 1 training manual.

1.4: Mapping Exercise

In their model of posttraumatic stress counseling, Bourne and Oliver (1999) described the importance of helping the client to survey the full effects of the traumatic incident. The client is encouraged to "map out" these effects in visual terms, for example, using paper and pen, and to think about what has changed, what remains the same, what has been lost, and what has been introduced since the incident?

Case Example

Mary was involved in an armed attack at the superstore where she worked. She has been off work with high anxiety for the last 2 months. Her completed mapping exercise is shown below:

EMPLOYMENT	HOME LIFE
No longer going to work	Children have been a continuous strength, and I enjoy spending time with them
Occupational health nurse ringing weekly	Doing the school run is unchanged
Visiting GP for sick notes	I'm doing more housework
Lost my good sickness record	Relationship with grandmother is unchanged
Colleagues are ringing me for progress reports	Feel let down by husband and defensive when he talks about work
Still getting paid	Parents are fussing, and my mum doesn't talk about her own problems any more
No focus/structure to week/day	I like being at home (but not alone)
I miss the lunch breaks and camaraderie	
Feel panic at the thought of returning	

(continued)

EMPLOYMENT	HOME LIFE
See work as risky now, particularly thoughts of being around money or stock-taking when store is closed I worry about my capability for managing conflict like customer complaints Supervisors/culture changes seem threatening No longer feel valued by work	Don't watch TV now Would like to go away for a holiday but scared Don't want sex but want lots of cuddles—hubby doesn't know the difference so this causes conflict Okay about driving with kids but must put music on and lock the doors

SOCIAL LIFE	TIME ALONE
Friends are sympathetic but awkward Not as much face-to-face contact with work friends Strangers appear threatening People at school gossip—feel labeled No longer going to the gym Feel okay about having people round to the house so long as they don't want to go over the robbery Feel okay in crowds—never used to but I seek company out (so long as they don't ask questions about why I'm not at work) Am only able to go shopping with a companion	Don't like open spaces Taking pills and have panic attacks I flit from one job to another, sometimes I clean like mad as a distraction Still like spending time with my children Jumpy at front door bell/telephone Don't like being alone—used to Uncomfortable about coming back to house especially after dropping kids at school Comfort eating—put on 1 stone Unhappy with self-image Nightmares

1.5: Identifying Symptomatology Using the Film Script

Using the metaphor of writing a film script, the client is asked to consider how life was before, during, and since the incident. This will include symptomatology, lifestyle, and any ways that his or her life has changed—the exercise should help provide a detailed narrative of life in the client's shoes, past and present.

BEFORE

DURING

AFTER

2 Fail to Plan—Plan to Fail

The therapist needs to help the client to identify and practice appropriate coping strategies that will support the client throughout the therapy. This chapter discusses the client's ability to self-regulate and handle high levels of affect. To give informed consent, the client should understand the process of EMDR and what to expect from sessions. This groundwork should be transparent and empowering and may involve further psychoeducation to ensure the client is actively engaged. During this time, a safe therapeutic relationship is being built and the client's confidence in, and understanding of, EMDR is increasing. EMDR can be a difficult concept to explain, and this chapter considers explanations at various levels. Therapists need to address any fears that the client (or therapist) may have about the later desensitization. Failing to do this can result in problems later.

IDENTIFYING AND PRACTICING APPROPRIATE COPING MECHANISMS

The maintaining factors of the effects of trauma- or anxiety-based disorders include fear, avoidance, and loss of control. Building or reinforcing coping strategies allows the client to regain some sense of control over what is happening, which, in turn, can have a positive impact on the fear and avoidance.

⊘ *Whatever You Do, Don't Do This . . .*

Julie's client had come specifically for EMDR treatment, having read an article on its success with anxiety. She became impatient with Julie's attempts at history taking and client preparation, saying, "I've come for EMDR—why are we wasting time on all this? Money's tight—can we just get on with it please?"

As Julie was a relatively novice EMDR therapist, she gave in to the pressure and proceeded with a desensitization session. Her client abreacted during this session and, without appropriate understanding of the process and coping strategies, dropped out of therapy saying EMDR had made her feel worse.

↘ *Common Pitfall*
Working With Mental Health Professionals

Many novice EMDR therapists report additional performance anxiety when their client is a mental health professional. The pressure to "get on with it" can be inadvertently increased by this client group. The sense of conscious incompetence is increased with a client who, it is feared, may become an observer of performance and technique.

The therapist treads a fine line between making assumptions about the client's depth or accuracy of understanding and patronizing the client: "I've read all about EMDR so you don't need to explain—I know how it works."

Another misplaced assumption may be that the mental health professional has (and, more importantly, uses) coping strategies: "Yes, I know about stress management and breathing techniques. You don't need to spend time on that."

Clarification of the need to follow the protocol at the initial contracting stage can assist here. It can also be helpful to ask such clients to describe in some detail their coping strategies and their understanding of EMDR. This can be presented as the therapist's need for working safely and professionally, and the mental health professional will respect that.

As EMDR can initially create additional disturbance to that already present, the client should be prepared for this both during and after sessions. Some clients will have limited or maladaptive coping strategies, and the preparation phase needs to encourage them to use a range of self-care strategies. What works for one person may not suit another. The therapist should ensure not only that clients have appropriate coping strategies but also that they are committed to using them, can do so successfully and are practicing them regularly. When therapists are working with individuals who are on the road to recovery compared with past functioning, there can be a fear of returning to dysfunction or addictive behavior once desensitization starts. To alleviate this anxiety, it is important that the client is clear about and confident in his or her coping strategies.

After a detailed history taking, therapists will be aware of the presenting symptomatology and can tailor the information their clients need to understand and manage their reactions.

Hyperarousal

Hyperarousal after a traumatic experience is normal. It occurs when a person's brain believes that person is at risk again because it misreads an external signal or trigger. It therefore responds as if the dangers currently exist and again releases the stress hormones into the system.

Typical symptoms include:

- Difficulty falling or staying asleep
- Irritability or angry outbursts
- Difficulty concentrating
- Exaggerated startle response—overreaction to loud noises or sudden movements

Hypervigilance

While the release of stress hormones at the time of the experience was appropriate and possibly saved the person from serious harm, the continual, incorrect release of these chemicals places the body's nervous system under extreme pressure and can be extremely distressing. Van der Kolk, McFarlane, and Weisaeth (1996) and Van der Kolk (2006) explain hyperarousal as a continual reaction to certain physical and emotional stimuli, as if still under the constant threat of danger. They suggest that people with PTSD tend to move immediately from stimulus to response without realizing what has made them upset. Consequently, they respond

Case Example
Psychoeducation and Coping Strategies

Ken was a police officer who had been shot at by an armed robber. He told his therapist Bill how he had been chasing the man down an alleyway when the man turned and fired at him, at very short range, missing him by inches. Ken described his reaction at the time and since:

> I didn't hear the shot. Everything felt very surreal and in slow motion as he turned to face me. I remember thinking...he won't shoot me—I'm a cop....I didn't feel anything, quite calm really. I was focused on his face not the weapon and it was like time stood still for ages, no one else was around, just the two of us in this little space. Since then I've struggled to piece the details together and work out why I didn't do certain things. What was wrong with me that I couldn't react? It's made me lose confidence in myself. I couldn't even tell the investigating officers what type of firearm it was. Now I just keep seeing his face and I have this overwhelming fear that he's still out there looking for me. I don't feel safe and worry about my family too, in case he comes for them.

Bill spent a large part of this session educating Ken about mental mobilization (Dyregrov, Solomon, & Bassoe, 2000) and normalizing the fight/flight/freeze reaction (Chapter Resources 2.1 and 2.2). During this, Ken gained confidence about revealing further symptoms that he had not relayed previously due to embarrassment:

> My wife took me out for a meal the other night to try and take my mind off things and I looked at the menu...and looked some more...and it was like—I can't even take this in, let alone make a decision! I thought I was losing it, going mad. The other thing that's strange is when you said this stress reaction can cause skin complaints because I've developed a rash across my chest that's been really worrying me. I wish I'd known earlier that these were related to the incident. I've felt like I was falling apart.

Spending this time with Ken reassured him that his symptoms were normal and began to give him some sense of control over them. Bill could then offer the rationale for how particular coping strategies would help manage Ken's hyperarousal. This ensured that Ken was motivated to use them.

to minor triggers with intense negative emotions and can overreact and become aggressive to others or shut down and freeze. This continued behavior appears to cause difficulty with attention and concentration. Van der Kolk et al. also indicate that this has an impact on information processing, with the individual constantly focusing on perceived and/or real sources of danger. This, in turn, causes sleep problems, for two reasons: first, the person is unable to relax, and, second, the person wants to avoid nightmares when he or she does sleep. Van der Kolk et al. (1996) go on to suggest that if this continues for a long time, the world becomes a very unsafe place for the individual. This is because, under normal circumstances, the autonomic arousal alerts the person to pay attention to potentially important situations. However, in a person who has PTSD, the warning signals become the "boy who cried wolf," and consequently the individual becomes increasingly unable to rely on bodily sensations as a warning against possible threat. Then the neutral triggers and the normal physical sensations may take on a new meaning and the person's own physiology becomes a source of fear. This incapacity to decipher messages from the autonomic nervous system impedes a person's ability to explain his or her feelings, and some people revert to earlier coping strategies for dealing (or not) with traumatic stress.

Clients often fear they will be overwhelmed by panic or physical symptoms once they begin to target the traumatic memories. If their levels of arousal are already raised, and EMDR raises them further, then there has to be a mechanism for keeping this within safe levels. They may feel out of control and as though they are going mad. Increased hyperarousal as the client begins to work on a traumatic event can lead to an increase in nightmares and flashbacks. Therefore it is imperative that hyperarousal is addressed before any EMDR processing takes place. Not attending to this phenomenon could catapult the client into a panic situation when starting the desensitization phase of EMDR, which could trigger a major abreaction and/or panic attack, or the client could walk away from therapy. Just as it is important that clients feel as safe as possible within the therapy and have confidence in the therapist, it is important that they learn and can demonstrate the use of self-soothing techniques prior to any desensitization. When hyperarousal is prolonged and is causing distress, it may be appropriate to take medication; this should be discussed with the client's physician.

The neurobiology of the traumatic response can also be explained using metaphors such as those of Scott (2008), who explains that the brain's alarm (the amygdala) is similar to an oversensitive house alarm,

---

$\oslash$ *Whatever You Do, Don't Do This...*

Joe had returned from Iraq and was experiencing flashbacks, nightmares, and irritability. He had been sent for therapy, and the practitioner had just completed level 1 of his EMDR. He thought the client had PTSD and in his eagerness to help told the client that he had just finished some training in a new therapy for PTSD that could help. Obviously, Joe was willing to try anything; however, when the processing started, because it was too overwhelming for him, Joe froze and blocked everything out. He didn't return to therapy.

---

suggesting that although it would detect a burglar breaking in, it unfortunately goes off when a football hits the window or a thunderstorm rolls in. Just like the house alarm can be reset, it is possible to reset your oversensitive personal alarm.

So, the first thing for the client to understand is that this is an automatic body response—a reflex. It is absolutely normal. The therapist can help to reduce the severity and impact by assisting the client in understanding what is happening.

Chapter 3 details resource building for complex trauma, but many of these techniques can be useful with all clients. As with any therapy that may elicit strong emotions, EMDR clients may need to be helped to stay grounded.

Staying Grounded

Grounding techniques can be taught very easily to clients and are another tool to help the client prepare for dealing with a possible abreaction while undergoing EMDR therapy. As a reminder, here is a summary of some of the methods that may be used:

- Using all your senses to be aware of your physical environment and then talking to others about it
- Being aware of your physical body and how you look
- Being aware of your movements in space as you walk
- Exercising while being aware of what you are doing
- Making a plan for the day and sharing that plan with another

- Challenging yourself to a contest to increase the length of time you can remain in the present
- Watching television and telling yourself or others what you saw
- Doing routine activities in a different way, for example, cleaning up the house in a different order
- Asking others to help you stay connected to them
- Talking to yourself about the present
- Planting your feet as firmly as you can on the ground in the here and now and feeling the physical sensations of doing this task.

Source: Williams, M. B., & Poijula, S. (2002). *The PTSD workbook.* Oakland, CA: New Harbinger Publications.

Safe Place

The purpose of the safe place is to provide the client with a self-soothing technique to manage high levels of emotional arousal both during and between sessions. However, creating a safe place may not be straightforward. When choosing a safe place, it is better for clients to choose a place that is not known to them in the here and now. To prevent contamination of any safe place, it is also best to avoid including known individuals—animals or humans; for example, it is best to avoid creating a safe place featuring a beloved dog that later dies.

There can be performance anxiety in creating a safe place. Not all clients, or therapists, are comfortable with guided imagery. Some may have difficulty using imagination or visualization techniques. Any self-soothing technique should be tailored to the client's abilities and level of comfort. Chapter 3 provides further information on this topic.

EXPLAINING EMDR THEORY

It is important that the client understands as much as possible about EMDR before engaging in the process.

EMDR's adaptive information processing (AIP) model posits that most psychopathology has its roots in distressing past experiences that have not been adequately processed (Shapiro, 2005). When new information is not processed adequately, the associated thoughts, images, emotions, and physical sensations are incorrectly stored, remaining intrusive or overwhelming and leading to current dysfunctions.

EMDR is thought to facilitate adaptive information processing, which involves the forging of associations between the dysfunctional stored material and more adaptive memory networks. This leads to a

Case Example
Managing Hyperarousal

Kevin was a security guard who had been attacked while patrolling premises at night. His levels of hyperarousal were very high, and his therapist Sarah helped him address these in various ways.

Education and Normalization
This helped to reduce Kevin's anxiety about the anxiety, built a sense of control, and motivated him to use the strategies that he had been taught while in therapy.

Encourage Exercise
Exercise should be tailored to each client's present capabilities. For Kevin, an important step forward was restarting his sessions at the gym. This helped him to burn off the excess adrenalin as well as release mood-enhancing endorphins. It was also a useful step toward building a structure to his days and slowly rebuilding his social contacts. He felt as though he was doing something positive for his recovery.

Self-Talk and Affirmations
Sarah encouraged Kevin to use these to remind himself that he was not in danger. Saying it out loud seemed strange at first, but Kevin later reported that it was an effective way of reinforcing that the danger was over.

Reducing Stimulants
Once he understood how he was reacting physically, Kevin was much more willing to reduce his use of stimulants such as caffeine and alcohol. He no longer saw them as helpful and began working with his body rather than against it.

Identify Triggers
The trauma survivor's triggers and emotional responses are likely to be negative and return him or her to the feelings of fear and vulnerability experienced at the time of the trauma. Sarah helped Kevin to identify the triggers associated with the attack—darkness, being alone, certain types of people, and his work environment. To manage hyperarousal, it is important to understand what is creating the trigger and to reeducate the brain that it is a faulty trigger and does not present a real current danger; that is, the danger is in the past.

Sarah helped him to plan homework tasks that would give him a small sense of success and empowerment. This helped Kevin gain confidence in himself and the therapeutic process and gave Sarah an indication of his motivation and ability to take action.

Case Example
Relaxation Techniques

Steve's need to project a strong façade meant he resisted the "touchy feely stuff" and had dropped out of relaxation classes for this reason. He stated that he couldn't relax in front of people without feeling "stupid." He resisted safe place exercises, guided visualizations, and even breathing techniques.

The therapist wanted to ensure that his arousal was manageable and was also concerned that Steve might block the later desensitization sessions if he felt his emotions rising in front of another person.

Additional time was spent on education about PTSD and normalizing potential emotions. Therapy also focused on emotional intelligence and where Steve's fears around emotions had originated. Slowly Steve relaxed in the presence of his therapist to the point where he could allow her to see him feeling vulnerable. Although this meant that preparation was lengthy and often repetitive, it was time well spent, and Steve's desensitization sessions went smoothly.

Case Example
Safe Place

Anthony was a veteran with PTSD who initially struggled to create a safe place. Prior to enlisting in the military, he had had a chaotic childhood and reported that he had never felt safe. The very title of the safe place exercise proved an insurmountable obstacle. In addition, Anthony had an overwhelming need to be vigilant to protect his loved ones. Relaxation of any form went against this urge as "something might happen."

His therapist changed the name of "safe place" and asked him to imagine instead a "timeout" space. Anthony created a "bubble" into which he could retreat and recover. An important part of this was that, once he entered the bubble, the external world stopped and time was paused so that no harm could come to others during his time out.

Anthony was able to practice this (for very short periods at first) but, as his hyperarousal decreased, both he and his therapist were able to build on this success.

> ⅏ *Common Pitfall*
> *Many Novices Have Difficulties Explaining the Process*
>
> How do you introduce EMDR to your clients? Some clients will want a very technical explanation to feel confident in their therapist's expertise. This may be wholly inappropriate for a client whose poor concentration and focus mean it is hard to grasp the concepts. Metaphors and visual aids can be useful, particularly if this is something the client can take away. Information sheets should be tailored to different levels of understanding, and therapists may wish to practice their explanation on a friend and ask for feedback.
>
> Remember that if you're not fully sure of the explanation, it will be very difficult to convince another person that EMDR can help. Ask accredited practitioners or consultants for their advice on explanations. If you still don't understand, don't feel bad about asking for clarification. It's all too easy to pretend we understand and to avoid asking the "stupid questions" on a training course, but we owe it to our clients to be able to translate the explanations for them.
>
> It is important that the client understands the process to be able to make an informed choice and "buy in" to the process.

reduction in emotional distress, learning, and making sense of an experience (Shapiro, 2005). One of the effects of AIP is the transformation of the negative self-concept, with its associated disturbing material, into a more realistic, appropriate, and adaptive view. However, clients differ in their ability to understand this theory, and therapists need to have a range of methods for delivering this explanation.

EMDR in Simple Terms

The theory behind EMDR can be difficult for a client to grasp, and therapists need to have a range of methods to describe it clearly and confidently, such as the following:

Usually when we have a disturbing experience, we sit and think about it, we dream about it, we talk about it, we acknowledge how we feel, and we reach completion. Thus the event is stored as a declarative memory, as a story. When we want to we can access the memory and talk about it as an experience from the past. With a traumatic event, there are profound physiological and psychological changes that block this adaptive processing, so we store feelings like shame, terror, and perception of the event, changes in thoughts and beliefs, and other strong feelings, which is our sensory mode of memory. So when the memory is accessed we reexperience it as it happened then and as if it is happening now. Thus there is no adaptive resolution and it is alive today.

The following explanation uses a simpler metaphor:

Think of your memory system as represented by two islands joined by a bridge. On an ordinary day, small boatloads of information arrive on a regular basis at the first island and get carried across the bridge to the other island to be stored away in that island's storage system. However, when something traumatic happens, it is as though a cruise ship, laden with information, has arrived at the first island. All the attempts to transport this information across the bridge at the same time weaken the bridge, and only little bits of information can get across. Sometimes the bridge collapses and no information is transported at all. EMDR helps to transport the information, ensuring that it can be stored away adaptively.

Figure 2.1 offers another explanation of EMDR using a simple model of the memory system. The therapist can describe the two distinct

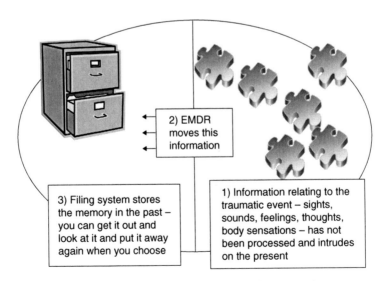

Figure 2.1 Simple metaphor for information processing

memory systems in the brain as a verbally accessible memory (VAM) and a situationally accessible memory (SAM). The SAM is composed largely of nonverbal data received during the occurrence of some kind of traumatic event. These data need to be integrated into the VAM with other memories, from where they can be retrieved as and when required (Brewin, 2003).

Yet another way to explain EMDR is by using the metaphor of defragging a computer. This is a particularly effective metaphor for computer-minded clients. The mind can be considered to be like the hard drive of a computer, where sometimes bits of data are stored in the wrong files, causing problems with running programs, occasional system shutdowns, and slow processing. Defragging the computer allows the information to be put in the right place so that the computer works efficiently.

Sometimes clients spontaneously come up with their own metaphorical explanation that therapists can work with. The main thing is that the client and the therapist share an understanding of traumatic memories and the EMDR process to which they can both relate.

Chapter 4 addresses in more detail further preparations for desensitization, how to explain this to the client, and what the client may actually experience. Because there can be a lot of information for the client to digest, the authors suggest that this is introduced gradually and reemphasized prior to the actual desensitization. To prevent overwhelming

---

❯ Common Pitfall
Scaring the Client (And the Therapist)

There is a big difference between ensuring your client has given informed consent to EMDR and creating fear about what could happen during desensitization.

Sometimes a therapist will spend a lot of time telling the client about potential abreactions, the surfacing of dissociated material, and the unknown aspects of EMDR processing. For example, "Once we start, we don't really know what could come up."

If you feel you may be discouraging clients, practice your script on a trusted colleague and ask for your colleague's reaction to it. Be aware of your manner when describing EMDR and try to appear confident and competent even if, as a novice, you don't totally feel this way.

the client with information about EMDR, it is important to provide bite-sized chunks supported by written information. The idea is to scaffold the information so that the client is not inundated with technicalities. It is always helpful to periodically review with clients their comprehension of the process.

HOW MUCH PREPARATION IS ENOUGH?

Chapter 1 outlined the importance of building a good therapeutic relationship. The authors consider that this enhances the process, and this continues throughout therapy. However, the depth of relationship and the time required to build it will vary from client to client.

One of the key supervision issues is whether the time is right to start desensitization. Conscientious therapists are very aware of the need to prepare well and build a safe therapeutic relationship. They can be reluctant to move forward with the protocol just in case they have missed something. There can also be an element of colluding with the client's avoidance. Just as chapter 1 emphasized that rushing in too early can create problems, overly delaying desensitization is undesirable. It can create frustration in both the client and the therapist and also magnify the eventual transition. Often it's a genuine fear of not being competent that keeps the therapist in the earlier phases.

Chapter 1 included the pre-EMDR checklist that therapists can use to ensure they have considered all the appropriate elements of preparation. The following is a summary of Emma's progress through Phase 2

> ⟫ *Common Pitfall*
> *Getting Stuck in Early Phases*
>
> The length of Phases 1 to 3 varies considerably from client to client. However, for those therapists who work within time-limited settings it is worth monitoring whether clients consistently don't progress to Phase 3 and beyond.
>
> If therapists find that they are always running out of sessions, it may be an indication that they are unnecessarily staying in the earlier phases because they have a fear of desensitization and are working within their comfort zone of usual therapy.

and a copy of her pre-EMDR checklist as completed by her therapist. By the end of Phases 1 and 2, Emma's therapist was beginning to formulate a treatment plan.

CASE STUDY

Emma's pre-EMDR checklist for any cautions before using EMDR.

CHECK	ANY COMMENTS
Has the client got suicidal thoughts or intent? Has he or she previously attempted suicide? Has the client reported current or previous self-harm?	No and no previous suicide ideation.
Does the client drink excessively, take drugs, gamble, or have any other comorbidity?	Previously, moderate social drinking only—none now.
	Reactive depression diagnosed by physician. No pharmacological treatment.
What does the client score on the dissociative experience scale (DES)?	19 (does not suggest the likelihood of a DD and no other signs are evident).
Are there previous critical events in the client's history?	Yes—see lifeline.
Does client know how to self-soothe? Can client manage high affect?	Meditation and listening to music.
	Encouraged further strategies and breathing techniques.
Have you enhanced a safe place and does client practice using it regularly?	Safe place enhanced and practiced—sitting on the end of a jetty watching the sun set.
If there is a current ongoing legal case, has legal advice been sought?	No, but I must be aware that there could be potential for this to change.
	My code of confidentiality does not require me to act on this information and I do not feel it would be in the client's best interests to do so.

(continued)

CHECK	ANY COMMENTS
Does the client have epilepsy?	No.
Any head injuries?	No.
Is the client pregnant?	Emma has tested negative for pregnancy and sexually transmitted infections following unprotected sex.
Any other medical condition? If so, does the client need to see a physician?	General good health.
Any medication? Prescription or otherwise	None.
Has the client been given literature on EMDR to take away, read, and research?	EMDR information sheet given and informative website addresses given.
What is the client's understanding of EMDR?	Emma sees EMDR as a way of helping her move on from the event. Likes the metaphor of computer defragging.
What (if any) are the client's expectations?	Emma hopes that EMDR will help her to feel safer and less to blame but has low expectations that this will happen.
What (if any) are the client's fears?	Initially, Emma was anxious about revisiting the childhood abuse but now feels ready and able to do so and cope with the effects. She is aware that she will be dealing with memories rather than having these events happen again.
Informed consent form signed?	Yes.
Check out preference for DAS—EM/audio/tapping	EM (second choice tapping).
If using eye movements, does the client wear contact lenses/glasses? Does the client have a history of eye diseases or surgeries?	No.

THERAPIST REFLECTIONS AT THE END OF PHASE 2

Emma had described her parents as caring but critical. She feels they wanted the best for her and for her to have the opportunities that they missed. She had one older brother who lived some distance away: "We were close but don't see each other much now." She had always done well at school and had plenty of friends. Her parents divorced when she was 8, although she stated that the divorce had been amicable and she always felt loved by both her parents. She stayed with her mother, but her father had good access.

Prior to the latest incident, she had been a popular, vivacious person with lots of friends and a good social life. She had excelled in her career and had been promoted through the ranks to become a well-respected manager within her field.

She appears to work hard to please those around her. Emma's symptoms would satisfy the diagnostic criteria for PTSD as laid out in *DSM IV* (American Psychiatric Association, 1994) and her physician has confirmed this diagnosis. Consequently, it was important to explain why she was experiencing those symptoms and learn how to manage them. From a combination of diagrams, metaphors, and information sheets on hyperarousal, sleep disturbance, reexperiencing, and avoidance, Emma has begun to make sense of her reactions. This is also helping her to identify triggers, and she has gradually started to face her fears, although she is still experiencing relatively high levels of anxiety. She had previously practiced meditation, and therefore found relaxation techniques and enhancement of the safe place easy to master. I have encouraged her to make use of these strategies, as well as breathing techniques and creative pursuits.

Emma has given informed consent to EMDR and I have addressed her concerns, assessed her emotional resilience and coping strategies, and explained the process and what may happen during and after desensitization, and together we have chosen the method of DAS. Emma was encouraged to research as much as she could about EMDR. This gave her a sense of regaining some control, as opposed to being a passive participant. All of this work has contributed to developing the therapeutic alliance, and I feel we have a good trusting relationship now.

Therapist Notes for Case Conceptualization

Emma's Symptomatology

- Poor concentration
- Sleep difficulties and nightmares
- Intrusive images during the day
- Hyperarousal
- Avoidance behavior (work, social activity)
- Lack of self-care

Early Memories That May Be Responsible for Laying the Groundwork for the Dysfunction

- Parents' divorce—Emma has no real recollection other than being shouted at by mother.
- What was said? How realistic is it that she has no recollection?
- Being "sent away" to live with aunt?
- Childhood molestation by cousin's friend
- Aunt's reaction to molestation—rejection, blame, not being protected
- Starting new school?
- Date rape

Present Triggers That Stimulate the Material

In brief, as given below, but we will need to identify specific situations and memories.

- Being alone at home
- Smell of alcohol or cigarettes on someone's breath
- Going out socially
- Getting dressed up and putting makeup on
- Being around men
- Questions about her medical leave
- Making simple mistakes such as forgetting to take her purse when shopping for food.

Desired Future Responses

- Be able to trust her own judgment
- Get back to work
- Be relaxed around men

- Be able to socialize with her friends as she once did
- Not to be so scared—how will she measure this?

Prioritizing Targets for Desensitization

- The themes Emma has relayed are as follows:

EVENT	THEMES
Parents' divorce	Possibly safety and responsibility? These are therapist hypotheses
Being shouted at by mother	Shame, responsibility
Being sent away	Rejection
Childhood molestation by cousin's friend	Safety Shame
Aunt's reaction to molestation	Blame Rejection Safety? Fear Shame
Starting new school	Rejection Fear
Road traffic accident	Blame (not apportioned – this was important)
Date rape	Shame Blame Safety

We could start with the rape. Is it too intense and would there be a risk of overwhelming Emma?

Would she benefit from some targeting to reduce its intensity? Would it be better to have a small success with an earlier memory of a distressing life experience that was not traumatic?

Are there feeder memories?

My judgment in this case is that the priority is to target the earlier events as there is a clear theme of responsibility that appears to be the overriding theme in her current presentation. These are possibly feeder memories. I would hope that there would be some generalisation effects that will reduce the later intensity when targeting the sexual assaults.

The initial target is Emma's mother shouting at her. Although she has no clear recollections of the divorce, her description of this event indicates that it could be an example of the conflict and tension in the home. Again, this could lead to generalisation.

FREQUENTLY ASKED QUESTIONS

Q: I have had a couple of clients with whom I have worked through Phases 1 and 2 who have then told me they are feeling much better and don't need anything further. They genuinely seemed to have made changes in their behavior and thinking, and in both cases I felt there was a good therapeutic relationship. However, I'm wondering if I'm doing something wrong as I didn't get to the desensitization?

A: Phases 1 and 2 are very important in their own right. Looking at what you accomplish during this time gives you an indication of the benefits to the client— psychoeducation, creating a safe place and resources, providing a therapeutic relationship, and helping to map out or talk through a client's history. For some clients, this will be enough for them to make their own changes, but see also box Common Pitfalls—Getting Stuck in Early Phases in this chapter. Chapter 3 discusses further preparation.

Q: My client has had EMDR before as well as a lot of other therapy. Do I need to go through the whole preparation phase again?

A: Can you be confident in the level of explanation that your client has previously received? In the preparation phase, you are also building the therapeutic relationship and reiterating coping strategies. There may have been significant developments between courses of therapy. If the client has done a lot of other therapy, his or her self-awareness can support the process, but it is important to remember that EMDR follows specific protocols. You may find you do not need to spend as long on preparation, but it still needs to be done.

Q: We have done all the preparation and my client has decided not to go ahead with EMDR. I don't want to force her into desensitization, so do I work on what is stopping her or change therapy?

A: We would suggest you first explore with your client her reasons for not wanting to go ahead with EMDR. These could include anxieties, lack of understanding, reduced affect, or changed goals for therapy, all of which you could work with. If the client still does not wish to use EMDR, you need to consider a different therapeutic approach or refer on.

LEARNING SUMMARY

You should feel confident that you are able to:

- Help the client identify adaptive coping strategies
- Ensure the client is able to self-soothe and that symptoms of anxiety are manageable
- Explain the process and theory of EMDR so that your client is fully informed and check whether his or her understanding is sufficient
- Ensure a good therapeutic relationship is in place
- Teach a safe place exercise and encourage your client to practice this.

RESOURCES

2.1: Mental Mobilization

Dyregrov et al. (2000) described mental mobilization as the increased capacity during emergency situations for the mind to process incoming information and refer to stored information. This has an adaptive survival function and knowledge of this can be empowering for clients who are struggling to make sense of their experience. Aspects of mental mobilization include the following:

- Focused attention on threat
- Intensification of sensory perception
- Mobilization of previous experience and training
- Rapid processing of information
- Memory enhancement of survival information
- Suspension of emotions
- Altered state of consciousness (feeling surreal)
- Altered time perception

Consequences of mental mobilization are as follows:

- Narrowed attention
- Loss of peripheral information and context
- Overvaluing of some details
- Distorted judgments
- Loss of sense of time and self-reference

- Memory gaps
- Emotional disorientation
- Intensified experience

2.2: Levels of Arousal

LEVEL OF AROUSAL	ADAPTIVE SURVIVAL RESPONSE	SYMPTOM
Low to moderate	Resting heart rate 60 – 80 beats per minute	
High (Heart rate around 110 – 145 beats per minute. Optimal survival and performance.)	The mind becomes focused and preoccupied with the perceived threat	Heightened awareness, time distortion
	Adrenalin and noradrenalin are released	Trembling of hands and legs as adrenalin turbocharges muscles ready for physical exertion, shaky voice
	The liver releases stored sugar to provide quick energy to the muscles. Heart pumps faster and blood pressure rises to carry fuel to large skeletal muscles.	Excess sugar in blood, high blood pressure, rise in body temperature
	Breathing becomes faster and more shallow in order to supply more oxygen to muscles	Overbreathing, tingling, asthma, chest pain
	Neck and shoulder muscles tense as the large skeletal muscles prepare for action	Fine motor skills deteriorate
	The body cools itself by perspiring: blood vessels and capillaries move close to the skin surface	Excess sweating, blushing
	Digestion slows down or stops as blood is diverted to muscles	Dry mouth, nausea
	Visual reaction time increases	Pupils dilate

(continued)

2.2: Levels of Arousal (continued)

LEVEL OF AROUSAL	ADAPTIVE SURVIVAL RESPONSE	SYMPTOM
Extreme (Heart rate rising to above 175 beats per minute)	Cognitive processing deteriorates as brain uses faster but more primitive processing routes. Survival option chosen automatically: gross motor skills at highest performance level for fighting or running from threat.	Fight/flight/ freeze response; seemingly "irrational" behaviour; complex motor skills deteriorate
	Senses are highly focused on area of threat	Loss of peripheral vision and hearing but heightened sensory awareness within that
	Vaso-constriction occurs so as to reduce bleeding from potential or actual wounds	Pallor
	Muscles at opening of bladder and anus are relaxed in preparation for possible evacuation: lightening the load in cases of flight	Desire to or actual emptying of bladder and/or bowels

2.3: Informed Consent Form

Consent for Eye Movement Desensitization and Reprocessing [Adapted from EMDR Institute Level 1 Training Manual (2005)]

EMDR has been recommended by the National Institute for Clinical Excellence as an effective treatment for PTSD. Research is emerging on its applicability to other psychological conditions. However, I understand that, although this treatment approach is widely validated, like all other psychotherapeutic approaches EMDR cannot claim to be 100% effective.

I have also been advised specifically of the following:

1. Distressing unresolved memories may surface during EMDR treatment and it is important that I give a full and open account to my therapist of past traumatic experiences.

2. Some clients have experienced reactions during EMDR treatment sessions that neither they nor their therapist may have anticipated, including a high level of emotion or physical sensations.
3. Following the treatment session, I may continue to process incidents/material, and other dreams, memories, flashbacks, feelings, etc., may surface.

Before commencing EMDR treatment, I have carefully considered all of the above. I have obtained any additional information and/ or professional advice that I deemed necessary or appropriate. I am not involved in any current or foreseeable legal proceedings in relation to the traumatic incident(s).

I hereby consent to receiving EMDR treatment.

Date:.....................................
Signature: ....
Full Name: ....

Complex Trauma and the Need for Extended Preparation

This chapter provides an overview of working with clients who present with more complex trauma. Many of the clients that come for EMDR will have a history of complex trauma or a chaotic childhood. We often get the clients that have tried many other therapeutic approaches. These have sometimes addressed the presenting symptoms (state changes), leading to temporary relief, while not necessarily resolving the underlying factors (trait changes.) The chapter expands on the additional preparation needed prior to using EMDR with this particular client group.

Dissociation, in various forms, is often seen in clients who have suffered extreme trauma or developmental issues. As stated in chapter 1, it is strongly recommended that EMDR is not used with clients who have Dissociative Disorders (DD) unless therapists are *confident and competent in both their EMDR practice and in working with this client population*. This chapter does not constitute training in DD but is intended to build awareness because some supervisees have not seen DD or worked with complex trauma prior to their EMDR training. Further reading, supervision, and training are highly recommended for anyone who finds themselves new to this area of work.

COMPLEX TRAUMA

The client with a one-off adult trauma is a fairly rare visitor to the EMDR practice. The recent trauma may be the presenting problem but during history taking it often becomes clear that this is the tip of the iceberg. Clients who have experienced complex trauma may lack basic life skills or have missed out on developmental stages due to a chaotic childhood, for example, parents who were absent, neglectful, or abusive. They may struggle with affect regulation, articulating emotions, and thoughts as well as relationship boundaries. The need for thorough preparation and history taking is vital. The therapeutic relationship must be secure enough for the client to feel safe before any direct work with traumatic memories begin. The amount of time needed for this will vary from client to client.

Rothschild (2000) suggests that one of the ways to increase the safety of trauma therapy is for the therapist to be very familiar with trauma theory; she states that teaching theory to clients and normalizing their experience is especially useful when the client has had multiple traumas and is not yet ready for anything else.

Assessing the complexity of the trauma and the stability, and available resources of the client is a useful first step. Shapiro (2001) refers to trauma in terms of large "T," the major, obvious traumatic incident; and small "t" traumas are disturbing life experiences. Parnell describes these "t traumas" as "those experiences that give one a lesser sense of self-confidence and assault one's sense of self-efficacy." (Parnell, 2007, p. 4)

Terr considers trauma in terms of Type I and Type II (Terr, 1994). Type I refers to a single one off trauma such as a road traffic accident or natural disaster. The experience of repeated or multiple traumatic events would be classed as Type II trauma.

Clients can further be considered in terms of their stability and capabilities (Rothschild, 2000; Schore, 1996; Terr, 1994). Type IIA describes clients with a relatively stable background who are able to distinguish a single trauma and their reactions to it from another that they have experienced. They are able to isolate and process each traumatic incident at a time during therapy. The treatment plan may utilize prioritizing and clustering (see chapter 4).

Type IIB describes clients who have suffered multiple traumatic events and become so overwhelmed with memories of them that they are unable to separate one traumatic event from the other. Rothschild further separates such Type IIB clients into those who are resourced, Type IIB(R), and nonresourced, Type IIB(nR).

Resourced clients are described as having had a stable background but who, because of their multiple and overwhelming trauma history, have lost their resilience.

The nonresourced client usually has trauma that originated in early childhood. For such clients, the early protocol stages can take considerable time and should not be rushed. A transparent approach, clear boundaries, and safety will help lay solid foundations.

Case Example
The Resourced Client

John's parents died suddenly when he was 13. He went from a warm, loving environment to be cared for by an elderly aunt. She was cold and distant, and John struggled to adapt to his new school. He was bullied mercilessly but found no comfort at home. When he was 31, he was involved in a serious accident at work during which he witnessed two colleagues being killed. This triggered an overwhelming array of negative and confusing emotions combined with panic attacks which he could not understand. He started to have suicidal thoughts and it was at that point that John decided to seek help.

It was important in the early stage to build understanding and control because initially John was extremely wary of trusting anyone. However, because the therapist's intention was to be as transparent as possible throughout the process, once John understood her way of working, he became more open and his body language gradually became visibly more relaxed. He later disclosed a sense of relief. He appeared to be overwhelmed and frightened by how his panic was taking over his life and wanted to make some active changes. By using psychoeducation, he began to understand why his body was responding in particular ways, and this brought some sense of order to the chaos.

Once he was able to manage his symptoms, he was keen to move toward desensitization. The therapist helped him to identify and reconnect with the resources from his early childhood.

Case Example
The Nonresourced Client

Harry's childhood had been chaotic. His mother had been a drug addict and he was neglected, often going without food, warmth, and basic affection. Her various partners were transient and, without exception, cruel to and dismissive of him. He spent considerable time in foster care while his mother attempted detox and rehabilitation but was usually returned to his home and the cycle began again. Harry did not know what it meant to be loved or to trust anyone. On leaving school, he joined the armed forces and for the first time in his life had a sense of stability and discipline. Although his core esteem remained low, he functioned well in the army environment. Unfortunately, his service came to an end following several traumatic incidents which left him with PTSD. This was undiagnosed but his rage, isolation, and depression led to him abusing alcohol and being discharged.

For many veterans, there is a huge stigma around accessing mental health services and Harry was no exception. He was therefore ambivalent about attending and cynical about the therapeutic relationship. His childhood memories were fragmented and unraveled in stages through the therapy. These new targets were added to his treatment plan.

Working with Harry on a positive model of coping with life was important. He had never experienced feelings of safety or love and his self esteem was rock bottom. Having mental health problems and accessing therapy called into question his very identity.

Harry felt "weak, soft, and pathetic" and needed a pragmatic, "nuts and bolts" approach. However, at the end of therapy, it was clear that the safe, trusting relationship that had developed had provided him with a much needed positive model of how life could be.

CHALLENGES TO THE THERAPEUTIC ALLIANCE

In addition to the *DSM IV* (American Psychiatric Association, 1994) diagnostic criteria for posttraumatic stress disorder, Herman (1992) describes further symptoms that may result from complex trauma. These can have an impact on the relationship in various ways.

Difficulties Regulating Emotions and Impulses

Clients may not have been taught how to regulate their emotions in early childhood. They may present with impulsive, risk-taking, or suicidal behaviors. One such case was that of Katrina who attended therapy because she had lost her temper and hit her teenage daughter. Although she had shouted angrily at her daughter in the past, she was horrified that this had escalated and was experiencing shame and guilt. Her difficulties in modulating anger were typical of complex trauma. During the assessment Katrina disclosed that she had been emotionally and physically abused by her father, and her mother was emotionally distant. As a child she was not allowed to express negative emotions and had developed passive aggressive behavior when she was angry. As an adult, although she was still very angry with her parents, she was a people pleaser and avoided conflict at all costs outside the home; if she sensed any prospect of conflict or criticism at work, she would panic and almost freeze (chronic affect dysregulation). However, because Katrina had a distorted sense of criticism, initially this made the therapeutic relationship extremely difficult because she saw any challenge, no matter how gentle, as threatening; in addition, because she was eager to please, she was not always honest with the therapist. It took a lot of work for the therapeutic alliance to develop to the point where Katrina felt she could trust the therapist and be herself without any adverse consequences.

Alterations in Self-Perception

These can involve feelings of being permanently damaged and carrying chronic guilt and shame. During an assessment session, John disclosed, almost as a throwaway remark, that while he was living in a children's home, he had been sexually abused on several occasions by one of the older residents. He stated that it was in the past and there was no point dragging it all up, because he had moved on with his life, thus minimizing the importance of the traumatic event in his life. He had never told anyone about this, not even his wife, because he always felt that it was his fault and that noone would understand. Furthermore, because the other resident had also been male, he questioned his sexuality and ultimately his whole identity. It took a long time for John to tell his story, and fully understand and normalize his reactions. He learned how to manage his symptoms and it was at that point John decided he was ready to move forward using EMDR to process the memories.

Somatization

Many clients who have suffered complex trauma carry their memories somatically. They may only be partially aware of prior traumatic incidents or have suppressed them completely. They may have physical ailments that have been labeled psychosomatic and in some cases, effectively dismissed. These can be wide-ranging and include chronic pain, fatigue, digestive problems, sexual symptoms, and unexplained long-term tension and pains. For many years, Bill suffered from debilitating irritable bowel syndrome and panic attacks. He had been seen by several hospital specialists but tests had found no underlying medical condition. Bill found it very difficult to make a link between his physical symptoms and psychological state. This lead to ambivalence about working on his trauma history as he believed he had a medical condition that was being missed by everyone he saw.

Alterations in Perception of the Perpetrator

This can include idealization of the perpetrator, becoming preoccupied with revenge or accepting the perpetrator's way of viewing the world. Sam, for example, had internalized the distorted beliefs of the man who abused him as a child. He believed that he must have somehow caused the abuse himself. His abuser had been a man of very good standing in the community and began by showing Sam affection whereas his own family was physically and emotionally abusive. The perpetrator had arranged for Sam to have trials with a major football club and Sam had gone on to play professionally. He found this paradox difficult to handle. The perpetrator often treated him kindly, but after each episode of abuse, told Sam that it was his fault and he was a shameful, wicked boy for leading him astray. Sam carried this shame and guilt into adult life.

Alterations in Relations With Others

Clients may present with an inability to trust and difficulties maintaining appropriate boundaries. This can lead to revictimization, for example, always finding themselves in abusive relationships or being taken advantage of in other ways. Jennifer had been physically and emotionally abused as a child and bullied at school. She went on to several relationships where domestic violence was an issue and complained of being bullied at work. She had "learned" from an early age that her role in life was to be a victim. Her therapist discussed the drama triangle with her and how she could break out of this role. It is important to recognize when clients are pulling us, as the therapist, into the role of rescuer, persecutor, or even victim.

Alterations in Systems of Meaning

Clients can find their underlying beliefs shattered and a loss of faith in the meaning of life. They may have feelings of complete despair and hopelessness. Carol had been sexually abused between the ages of 9 and 12 by a family member. She was raped at age 14 by a stranger and in her adult life had a succession of physically and emotionally abusive relationships. She presented in therapy with a sense of despair that this was how life was meant to be for her. Her hopes and sustaining beliefs gradually had been eroded. For her, the world was full of bad things and bad people.

Ultimately the further along the spectrum our client is, the more preparation will be needed before using EMDR. Consequently, it is important that the therapy is tailored to suit the individual needs of the client, and, as Rothschild (2000) states, should take into account factors such as existing levels of emotional development, their ability to progress in therapy, and the complexity of the issues involved.

RESOURCE BUILDING FOR MORE COMPLEX TRAUMA

Before carrying out the desensitization phase of EMDR, individuals need to have an adequate level of resilience and be sufficiently resourced (Leeds, 2009). This will increase their ability to adaptively change state by enhancing their access to functional memory networks. This enhancement of current functioning is particularly relevant when working with clients at the more complex end of the trauma continuum. It is important to consider factors such as lower levels of functioning, instability, lack of or maladaptive coping skills, internally or externally chaotic systems, and whether the client is able to tolerate high affect. Identifying any fears around losing control, going mad, becoming violent, or not being able to stop the sadness are, as with any other therapy, issues that need to be addressed explicitly prior to processing the traumatic incident(s).

Methods

There are various methods to help clients build resources, and, as an experienced therapist, the reader will already have useful skills in place to facilitate this process. This section provides a compilation of some of the ideas drawn from a range of approaches. However, it is important to recognize and acknowledge the individuals' fortitude, because sometimes, it can be easy to forget how resilient clients already are, having survived up to this point in their life. Consequently, the first step in resource building is to ascertain the individuals' current ability to cope and help them to identify their strength and capabilities. Chapter 4 describes the importance of identifying the clients' fears around processing the memories. During preparation, clients can be asked what they may need to allay those fears and help them through the difficult times. This will need to be reviewed and built on regularly. Generally, the more resources an individual has, the better.

Traditional stress management techniques are helpful coping strategies. These may include teaching breathing techniques, progressive muscle relaxation, meditation, and yoga. Herbert Benson (2000) described the "relaxation response" as a distinct physiological state which is the opposite of the way a body reacts under stress or during a panic attack. It is suggested that the regular daily practice of deep relaxation provides numerous benefits including a generalization of relaxation to all aspects of an individual's life. A sample script for a progressive relaxation with guided imagery is given in Resource 3.1.

The safe place exercise was introduced in chapter 2. It is an important resource in EMDR therapy and the client should be able to access this independently and under guidance. It may be used during desensitization when the client is in danger of becoming overwhelmed by affect, to close an incomplete session, and between sessions. However, there are several points that need to be considered when clients are choosing their safe place.

- Some clients have never known anywhere "safe," so may need a different label such as "calm space."
- If possible, it is helpful for clients to be alone in the safe place that is without someone they are close to, or a pet. This is because if anything happens to the other person/animal the safe place can become contaminated.
- It may be better to choose an imaginary place which is not known to the client in the here and now. Avoid secret places if possible.
- The therapist may make suggestions, for example, on top of a mountain, watching the sunset, various natural settings but must ensure that none of these scenarios contain triggers that may raise anxiety levels.

- Some clients are uncomfortable with their eyes closed, so should be offered the option of focusing on a spot on the ceiling, wall, or floor.
- Once the safe place is decided, check in with the client if there is anything that is not working or does not feel right and give them the opportunity to change it.
- Let clients know that they can change the safe place at any time they wish.
- The therapist should test out the clients' ability to access their safe place under guidance. Clients should then be able to practice moving to and from their safe place, possibly by use of a cue word or action. Finally, the client should practice using the safe place to manage a mildly disturbing scenario.
- Clients should be encouraged to incorporate any extra "security" measures that are needed to provide safety. For example, a client may wish to have a walled garden with a locked gate where he or she has the only key or an alarm system that will summon immediate assistance.
- If you are using DAS to enhance the safe place, the client needs to be aware that this can sometimes initiate the processing of disturbing material. It is important to note that when enhancing any resource with DAS shorter sets (4–6) should be used. If any neutral or even negative feedback is offered by the client, the therapist should stop this procedure.

Some clients may benefit from extended resource development as described by Kiessling (2005).

⊘ *Whatever You Do, Don't Do This...*

John struggled to come up with a safe place and his therapist suggested a beach scenario. John was hesitant to go with this but, in the absence of an alternative, agreed to give it a go. What he had not yet revealed to his therapist was that he had been sexually assaulted in sand dunes while on a family holiday. John had not felt ready to disclose this because the therapeutic relationship was in its early stages.

If the client shows any signs of hesitance or discomfort when creating a safe place, the therapist should stop and explore the underlying feelings.

Imaginary containers are another method of "holding" any disturbing memories. This can be done at the end of the session by asking the client to imagine a large box or safe with a heavy lid, and get them to imagine putting the memories into the container, putting the lid on, locking it, if appropriate, and leaving it in the consulting room until the next session.

Resource Building

For clients who have not had many positive experiences or role models in their life, it can help to channel the imagined resources of another person or animal. This does not have to be someone known to them, for example, it could be a superhero, a religious icon or figure, a television character, or a power animal, such as a lion. Avoid using someone close who has died, for example, a loving grandmother, because this may tap into unresolved grief. Some clients may suggest that they want the therapist as their resource. To prevent contamination, transference, or dependency, this should be discouraged. However, when all else fails, therapists

---

Case Example
Installing a Power Animal

Mary needed to be able to deal with changing relationships. Her therapist, Julie, explored with her the kind of qualities that she needed such as strength, inner calm, assertiveness, and resilience. Working first on the quality of inner calm, she then asked what animal could be described in that way.

Mary felt that a swan fit the bill. She viewed this animal as having a serene exterior apparently gliding effortlessly through life while being able to conceal the real work hidden below the surface. When asked, she imagined the swan surrounded by a pink aura of calmness.

Julie asked Mary to imagine sitting beside this image and to allow it to become merged with her. Mary was guided to notice the aura being absorbed through her skin, nose, and breath and to just let it fill her body.

The sensation of calmness was enhanced with DAS.

Julie repeated this process with the other qualities Mary desired.

may have to assume this role or be very creative. As the client improves in treatment, the client can be weaned from the imagery of the therapist as that resource.

Other Strategies

Self-care is important. Clients need to recognize that because they are going through a difficult time it is vital to look after their physical, emotional, and spiritual well being. The therapist can help them consider small steps that they can take to do this.

Journal work is useful to record feelings and understand trauma reaction. Some therapists may wish to use therapeutic writing or drawing. This can involve writing or drawing about how they felt before the trauma, what happened during the event, what they did and how they felt. Together, the client and therapist can look at areas that the client was in and was not able to control.

Future planning can help—revisiting what clients want to achieve from therapy—how will they feel/look/act when they have got through this? Clients can be guided in visualizing an optimistic future, free of any trauma reaction. Creating a "circle of intent" with all the things, large and small, that they want in their future can build a sense of hope and refocus on positive aspects. This exercise can reveal fears around even positive changes. It is not advisable to use this exercise where bereavement is a factor because it can exacerbate the sense of loss and isolation.

Clients can be helped to regain or recognize control in other areas of their life—work, home, children, pets, and play.

The rewind technique (Muss, 1991) is also a useful strategy (see Chapter Resource 3.2: The Rewind Technique).

Manipulating Images and Movies

Before working on a traumatic memory, try this technique with a clear but positive memory of an event that your clients have experienced. Begin by helping your clients to relax, focusing on their breathing and exhaling longer than the inhale, before guiding them as follows:

For "Movies"

Imagine you are watching the event on a TV screen.
Notice how this feels.

Then step further back and imagine watching yourself watching the TV screen.

Notice how this feels.

You can now help to further reduce the intensity of the images by guiding your client in blurring the screen, turning down the color, contrast, brightness, and volume, or reducing the size of the screen.

Finally you can turn off the TV.

For a Still Image

First, put the image in a frame and imagine you are in an art gallery seeing it on the wall.

Notice the shape, texture, color, and material of the frame.

Again, you can now help your client to further reduce the intensity of the images by blurring the picture, turning down the contrast, brightness, and changing from color to black/white or by reducing the size of the picture by increasing the size of the frame.

Finally, you can increase the frame so that the picture shrinks to a dot then nothing. (Alternatively, turn the picture to the wall or paint over it.)

Once clients have their "toolbox" of resources, they need to have the opportunity to test them out. By using SUDS to monitor the clients' level of tension in the session when teaching the technique, you are gently introducing the concept of SUDS. Clients can practice, gain confidence, and this will raise awareness of disturbance for those who

---

⊌ Common Pitfall
Overuse of Resource Enhancement

A good preparation is important but not a substitute for processing. Coping strategies and resource installation can have a big impact on the presenting symptoms (state changes), leading to temporary relief.

Clients may feel better and leave therapy without resolving the underlying factors (trait changes). When they later "relapse" they may have lost faith in EMDR as a therapy that promotes long-term results.

The therapist can feel that EMDR "worked" and begins to avoid desensitization and focus primarily on resource enhancement.

are detached from their emotions or body. It is also a method of illustrating control.

By encouraging the individuals to keep a journal to record such practice opportunities, they will begin a habit of chronicling their thoughts, images, bodily sensations, and feelings, ready for when desensitization starts. The client can be asked to just notice what is going on and report back using the spirit of experimentation, reiterating that we can learn from whatever happens.

Resource enhancement will vary from client to client depending on the complexity of their trauma history and their current coping skills.

WORKING WITH CLIENTS WHO DISSOCIATE

Dissociation exists along a continuum from normal everyday experiences to disorders that interfere with the individual's functioning. As stated in chapter 2, readers are encouraged to access one of the many comprehensive texts available (Dell & O'Neill, 2009; DePrince & Cromer, 2006; DePrince & Freyd, 2007; Forgash & Copeley, 2008; Karjala, 2007; Moskovitz, Schafer, & Dorahy, 2008; Nijenhuis, 1999; Ross, 1989, 1996; Steinberg, 1995; Watkins, 1997).

According to *DSM IV*, dissociation is a "disruption in the usually integrated functions of consciousness, memory, identity, or perception of the environment" (American Psychiatric Association, 1994, p. 477). Most of us will be familiar with a type of normal dissociation called absorption. Examples of this normal dissociative process are daydreaming, being in a world of our own, or "highway hypnosis" (driving a familiar route and getting to our destination without remembering part of the journey). For some people, dissociation was a traumatic defense that served to protect them from overwhelming pain and trauma and may even become a defensive pattern developed in childhood that continues into adulthood.

Many clients who come for EMDR will be experiencing primary levels of dissociation such as nightmares, flashbacks, and intrusions. They are unable to integrate the traumatic material into their personal memory and identity. Aspects of the sensory and emotional experience remain unprocessed.

Secondary levels—depersonalization and derealization are the dissociation between observing ego and experiencing ego, for example, mentally leaving your body and observing your life from a distance or seeing your current environment as "dreamlike" or surreal in some way.

Tertiary levels of dissociation would not respond well to the standard EMDR protocol. The client will have complex states separated by amnesic barriers as is the case with dissociative identity disorder (DID) where the individual has developed distinct personality states.

Dissociative Disorders

The American Psychiatric Association (1994) defines the following types of DD.

Dissociative Amnesia can occur during a traumatic event leading to acute loss of memory. For example, Janet was involved in a serious road traffic accident. She remembered a car coming toward her and the inevitability of a head-on collision, then being in the ambulance as paramedics tended her. She was later told by her passenger that she had indeed been conscious throughout but Janet had no memory of this. Clients such as Janet may be fearful of desensitization in case the full memory is retrieved and overwhelms them. They may fear feeling extreme pain memory, which is currently blocked.

With **Dissociative Fugue**, individuals suddenly and unexpectedly go on a journey. At its extreme, they may assume a new identity and name and are unable to recall important prior personal events. Kevan is an example of a less extreme case. He found himself in a location many miles from home with no memory of his journey, why he was there, or where in fact he was. He had to go into a store and ask the staff where he was. He was disoriented and confused.

⬎ *Common Pitfall*
Surfacing Memories

During desensitization, Sandra began to piece together the surfacing material and over-analyze their significance. She took material that was possible symbolic and used this to build a factual account of her childhood. Her therapist had not sufficiently explained that surfacing memories were not to be taken at face value because they are sometimes symbolic or not objectively accurate and felt increasingly helpless as Sandra began to pause desensitization to write down more "evidence."

Depersonalization Disorder may cause clients to feel detached from their own body, as though they do not belong in it, and are observers in their own life. This happens frequently enough and is at a level that causes great distress and impairs their general functioning. Paul would often find himself standing at the side of himself, commenting on his actions. He found this a frightening experience and worried that he was not fully in control of himself and that he was going mad.

Dissociative Identity Disorder (DID) used to be referred to as multiple personality disorder and is described as the most severe form of dissociative pathology (Kluft, Steinberg, & Spitzer, 1988). Clients with DID display at least two distinct and enduring "alters" or identity states that recurrently take control of their behavior. These disturbances are not accounted for by the use of substances (alcohol, drugs). These clients appear to have more than one "person" living within their body. The "alters" may differ in personality, age, gender, memories, and life histories. They may or may not be aware of each other. They may have differing goals and needs that are conflicting, for example, the need for intimacy versus the need for safety.

Lisa's childhood had been chronically abusive and she had developed DID. Her "alters" were identified as "Little Lisa," her traumatized 6-year-old child state, who was fearful and who panicked whenever anybody got close to her. "Big Lisa" was the competent, professional façade that she portrayed on a day to day basis. "Big Lisa" could go into meetings and be assertive but work was her focus and her area of control and safety. Play and fun were anathema to "Big Lisa" but "Sally" was the self-destructive alter in her early twenties, addicted to casual sex, and craving intimacy. She was hedonistic and undertook risks to satisfy her need to feel alive. "Peter" was a critical alter and would seek out punishing behavior such as excessive exercise and dieting, depriving Lisa of anything good in life because she did not deserve it. He would sometimes take executive control when Lisa looked in the mirror and demean her appearance and identity.

Up to 86% of people with DID express a "child alter" who is often traumatized (Ross et al., 1989). EMDR can disrupt the dissociative barriers between the "alters" and their specific memories and requires careful handling by a therapist trained in working with this population.

Dissociative Disorder Not Otherwise Specified (DDNOS) describes clients with DDNOS who do not meet the *DSM-IV* criteria for the above disorders but experience a change in the usual integrative functioning of consciousness, identity, or memory. Most often, clients having a diagnosis of DDNOS do not meet all of the criteria for a DID diagnosis (see also Ross et al., 1992).

Identifying Dissociative Disorders

There is a risk of harm to the client if EMDR is used without the appropriate safeguards. Therapists are advised to screen every client for the presence of an underlying DD. Methods for doing this include the dissociative experiences scale (DES; Bernstein & Putnam, 1986) and the mental status examination for DD (Loewenstein, 1991). (See also Frequently Asked Questions in this chapter.)

The DES is a 28-item self-administered questionnaire that takes around 10 min for the client to complete and the same for the therapist to score. Scores over 20–25 should raise the therapist's suspicions regarding the degree of dissociation in the client's day-to-day life and the possibility of a DD.

The DES measures dissociation on the continuum of normal, everyday experiences to pathological dissociation. Low scores on DES are as significant as high scores. For example, very low scores suggest that the clients are under-reporting their day-to-day experiences. Some level of dissociation (e.g. daydreaming, finding yourself in a room and not knowing why you went in there) is a normal experience.

The DES-Taxon (DES-T) (Waller, Putnam, & Carlson, 1996) focuses on the DES questions that consider those experiences that are more likely to be pathological. It consists of 8 of the DES questions: 3, 5, 7, 8, 12, 13, 22, and 27. The DES-T correlates roughly to the areas of depersonalization, derealization, amnesia, identity confusion, and identity alteration. Your client's DES-T score provides the probability that he/she dissociates pathologically.

Neither of these screening tools should be viewed as conclusive but rather indicate the probability of pathological dissociative symptoms and that the therapist should refer for further assessment utilizing one of the following—the structured clinical interview for DSM-IV DD revised (SCID-D Revised), the DD interview schedule—DSM-IV version (DDIS-DSM-IV) or the multiscale dissociation inventory [MDI] (Briere, 2002).

> Chronically dissociative patients are among the most complicated individuals to whom we provide treatment. They bring to psychotherapy a range of complicated issues regarding their past history of trauma and their current

functioning. Therefore, working with these clients will require additional training beyond EMDR which is only one segment of their treatment. (Gerald Puk, PhD, Psychologist)

FREQUENTLY ASKED QUESTIONS

Q: **My client completed a DES and scored 100% on a couple of items. There are no other indications of pathological dissociation and all her other scores were in the region of 0–20. Do the high scores mean I can't proceed?**

A: It is always useful to explore high scores with your client. For example, a client scored highly on item 19 (ability to ignore pain) was using techniques learnt in martial arts; another scored highly on item 24 (not remembering whether something has actually happened or he or she had just thought about it) and revealed that these were instances such as not being sure he or she had locked the front door and having to go back and check; a keen meditator scored highly on item 20 (sitting staring into space, thinking of nothing). Clarifying with your client can reveal whether this is misunderstanding of the DES statement, symptomatic of general anxiety and stress, or possibly reflect an underlying tendency to dissociate. Trauma can lead to general feelings of unreality and isolation and therapists may need to teach grounding exercises to clients before proceeding. If in doubt, seek specialist advice.

Q: **Should I use DAS to install safe place? I've heard of different safe place protocols and am worried I'm using the wrong one.**

A: There is no right or wrong safe place; therapists use a variety of methods to suit the individual client. Other methods include guided visualization, neuro linguistic programming anchoring techniques, and CDs. There are advantages and disadvantages to each one and therapists are advised to have more than one tool in their box. When using DAS to enhance the safe place, some therapists fear that negative material will surface or that clients will feel they can use self-directed DAS when accessing the safe place outside the therapy room. Conversely, the formal safe place protocol can provide a positive association with DAS for the client. The most important issue is that clients use a technique with which they are comfortable. Clients' use of self-soothing techniques outside the session can be a measure of how much they are opting in to the process, understand the psychoeducation, and trust the therapist.

LEARNING SUMMARY

You should feel confident that you are able to do the following:

- Recognize a client with a complex history of trauma
- Use a range of strategies to stabilize the client and manage strong emotions
- Identify the signs of a possible DD clinical profile. See also appendix of workshop manual of Shapiro (2001)
- Use a screening tool for all clients to ascertain levels of dissociation.

RESOURCES

3.1: SCRIPT FOR A GUIDED VISUALIZATION

Sit upright and well back in the chair so that your thighs and back are supported, and rest your hands on your lap or lightly on top of your thighs. If you like, take off your shoes, and let your feet rest flat on the ground. If you want to, close your eyes.

Begin by breathing out first. Then breathe in easily, just as much as you need. Now breathe out slowly with a slight sigh, like a balloon slowly deflating. Do this once more, slowly ... breathe in ... breathe out ... as you breathe out, feel the tension begin to drain away. Then go back to your ordinary breathing: even, quiet, steady.

Now direct your thoughts to each part of your body in turn, to the muscles and joints.

Think first about your left foot. Your toes are still. Your foot feels heavy on the floor. Let your foot and toes start to feel completely relaxed. Now think about your right foot ... toes ... ankles ... they are resting heavily on the floor. Let both your feet, toes, ankles start to relax.

Now think about your legs. Let your legs feel completely relaxed and heavy on the chair. Soften your thighs, soften your knees, relax and let them rest.

Think now about your back and your spine. Let the tension drain away from your back and from your spine. Follow your breathing, and each time you breathe out, relax your back and spine a little more.

Let your abdominal muscles become soft and loose. There's no need to hold your stomach in tight, it rises and falls as you breathe quietly—feel that your stomach is completely relaxed.

Your chest is calm and full of space. Let your breathing be slow and easy, and each time you breathe out, let go a little more.

Think now about the fingers of your left hand—they are curved, limp, and quite still. Now the fingers of your right hand ... relaxed, ... soft, and still. Let this feeling of relaxation spread ... up your arms ... feel the heaviness in your arms up to your shoulders. Let your shoulders relax, let them drop easily ... and then let them drop even further than you thought they could.

Think about your neck. Feel the tension melt away from your neck and shoulders. Each time you breathe out, relax your neck a little more.

Now before we move on, just check to see if all these parts of your body are still relaxed—your feet, legs, back and spine, tummy, hands, arms, neck, and shoulders. Keep your breathing gentle and easy. Every time you breathe out, relax a little more, and let all the tensions ease away from your body. No tensions ... just enjoy this feeling of relaxation.

Now think about your face. Let the expression leave your face. Smooth out your brow and let your forehead feel wide, and relaxed. Let your eyebrows drop gently. There's no tension around your eyes ... your eyelids gently closed, your eyes are still. Let your jaw unwind ... teeth slightly apart as your jaw relaxes more and more. Feel the relief of letting go.

Now think about your tongue and throat. Let your tongue drop down to the bottom of your mouth and relax completely. Relax your tongue and throat. And your lips ... lightly together, no pressure between them.

Let all the muscles in your face unwind and let go—there's no tension in your face—just let it relax more and more.

Now, instead of thinking about yourself in parts, feel the all-over sensation of letting go, of quiet, and rest. Check to see if you are still relaxed. Stay like this for a few moments and listen to your breathing ... in ... out ... let your body become looser, heavier, each time you breathe out.

And in your mind, I want you to imagine you are on a beach ... a quiet beach with soft, white sand and a gentle turquoise sea. This is your very own private beach and you can do whatever you need to make it perfect in your imagination. Look out toward the horizon and feel the space and freedom ... the feeling of endless time.

Feel the sand between your toes ... the sun on your back, warming you ... a gentle breeze on your face.

Listen to your surroundings ... you may hear a seagull cry ... the waves gently breaking on the shore ... or the light breeze rustling through palm trees.

Smell the sea air ... scents of tropical flowers and coconut sun oil.

Reach out in your imagination and run your fingers through the sand. Pick up a shell and feel its cool texture. Dip your toes in the water.

Run your tongue over your lips and taste the salt air.

Notice the feeling of complete relaxation, ... let it fill you up from the top of your head to the tips of your toes, ... warming and soothing. And just enjoy your time on this special beach for a few moments, soaking up the sunshine and peace.

And now, as you gently come back to the here and now, slowly, wriggle your fingers a little ... and your toes. Notice the feel of your feet on the floor. Listen to the sounds in and around the room. Imagine a cool breeze on your forehead. Yawn and stretch ... very slowly open your eyes, letting the light in gradually and becoming aware of the people around you. Sit quietly for a little while longer until you are ready to move, slowly and gently at first.

RESOURCE 3.2: THE REWIND TECHNIQUE

Before working on a traumatic memory, try this technique with a clear but positive memory of an event that your client has experienced.

Begin by helping your clients to relax, focusing on their breathing and exhaling longer than the inhale, before guiding them as follows:

1. Imagine that you are sitting in the centre of a totally empty cinema with the screen in front of you and the projection room behind you.
2. Now float out of your body and go to the projection room. See yourself sitting in the cinema, watching the screen. From the projection room, you can see the entire cinema as well as yourself.
3. You are going to watch two films. The first film replays the traumatic event as you experienced it or as you remember it in your dreams, flashbacks, or nightmares. You will see yourself on the screen as though someone had taken a video of you during the event. When you start the film, begin it at the point just prior to the traumatic event, seeing yourself as you were before it occurred. Remember, you are sitting in the cinema watching the

film, but you are also in the projection room watching yourself in the theatre as you watch the film.

4. So now play the film at its normal speed. Stop the film when you realized that you were going to survive or when your memory begins to fade.

5. Now we will watch the second film. This is called the rewind. You will not watch the rewind from the projection room but you will experience it on the screen, seeing it as though it were happening to you now, with all its sounds, smells, feelings, taste, and touch sensations. You are actually in the film, re-experiencing the event. However, you see and feel it all happening backward, from after the event until before the event happened. This re-experiencing takes practice and must be done rapidly. Remembering a trauma of about 1 min would mean having a rewind of about 10–15 s.

6. So now quickly try the rewind.

7. You may find rewinding hard to do initially. However, keep practicing until it feels right. After you learn the process, you can use the rewind every time you remember the trauma to scramble the sequence of events and to take you back to the starting point— the good image. As time goes on, the rewind process will happen faster and faster.

Debrief your client on how this felt for them and finish with a relaxation exercise.

[Adapted from Muss, D. (1991). *The Trauma Trap.* London: Doubleday.]

4

From the General to the Specific—Selecting the Target Memory

As highlighted in chapter 1, the treatment plan needs to identify specific targets for reprocessing. This will be a three-pronged approach that includes the **past** memories that appeared to have set the pathology in process, the **present** situations that, and people who, exacerbate this dysfunction, and the desired **future** response, emotionally, cognitively, and behaviorally. Clients and therapists need to understand the rationale for selecting a particular target utilizing prioritization and clustering techniques as illustrated with the case study. Choosing the correct target can involve some detective work, but this will be time well spent. Various methods of identifying the initial targets are offered, including the floatback technique and affect scan. This chapter guides practitioners on how to identify the components of a memory network for reprocessing. The chapter then focuses on the assessment phase and the importance of negative cognitions (NCs) drawing heavily on illustrative case vignettes. Many practitioners experience difficulty in getting the right NC, and methods for drawing out the NC are illustrated. Chapter 4 also considers final preparations prior to desensitization, identifying the positive cognition, rating the levels of subjective units of disturbance (SUD) and validity of cognition (VOC), emotional and physical responses, and working with the client's different levels of awareness and articulation.

A BELIEF BY ANY OTHER NAME

Janoff-Bulman (1985) introduced the notion of an "Assumptive World Theory" to describe how individuals make assumptions about themselves and the world they live in. Our fundamental assumptions of "I am invulnerable," "the world is just and makes sense," and "I am basically a good person" may be "shattered" when a traumatic event is experienced.

According to McCann and Pearlman's (1990) Constructionist Self-Development Theory (CSDT), people give meaning to traumatic events depending on how, as individuals, they interpret them. These interpretations of the traumatic events may result in disruptions in their cognitive schemas, that is, the way they view themselves and the world. Disruptions may occur in the psychological need areas of safety, trust, esteem, power, and intimacy.

Consider a police officer's personal experience of a violent assault during which he is injured and his colleague dies. Then, consider his potentially "shattered" assumptive world: "I am not invulnerable," "the world does not make sense, good people are not supposed to die," and "I don't believe I am a good person, I should have done something, I should have been able to prevent this." This shattering of assumptions can be one of the factors contributing to the cause of PTSD because of the anxieties that are raised when the world no longer makes sense.

As practicing clinicians, it is important to understand that our belief system permeates every aspect of our lives and helps us to create our identity. Consequently, when this belief system is shattered by a traumatic event it can have devastating implications for the individual.

Cognitive behavioral therapists (CBTs) will be familiar with terms such as core beliefs and cognitive schemas, but EMDR therapists come from diverse theoretical backgrounds and, although other therapies may not adopt this particular terminology, the notion is implicit within each theory.

Person-centered counseling (PCC; Rogers, 1995) refers to the "self-concept" describing the individual's self-image largely based on life experience and attitudes expressed by significant others, such as family, teachers, and friends. Rogers also refers to the "Ideal self," which is the way in which individuals would like to see themselves but which can differ radically from the self-concept. Again this can be formed through the internalized values of other people who tell these individuals how they should be rather than accept them for who they are.

Psychodynamic theory (PD), which originates mainly from Freud's study of human development, offers a variety of explanations. Thomas (1995) states that "internal worlds" are being created from birth (or even prebirth) by internalizing the external world. She suggests that at first the child's experience of the world is preverbal, and is often highly emotional. In addition, much of this early experience takes place in relationship with other human beings involving both verbal and nonverbal interaction. Consequently, this internal world begins to effect intention and behavior in the external world and shapes the meaning of later experiences. The key difference within the psychodynamic approaches is the emphasis placed on the respective roles of nature and nurture within this process of construction. Another assumption that psychoanalysts make is that we systematically distort our internal realities of the world so as to avoid anxiety (Thomas, 1997). This is carried out using "defense mechanisms" such as repression, denial, and projection; however, these are seen as largely unconscious processes.

So imagine for a moment the client who presents following a road traffic collision suffering from PTSD. During the history-taking phase you discover that her father had been a hard task master and the client had "never felt good enough" (identified as core belief, CBT, self-concept, PCC, or internal world, PD). Later in her life she had been married to a very dogmatic man who had very high expectations of her. The client had learned to cope with this by making sure everything was done to perfection and took control of every situation (also known as basic assumptions [CBT], ideal self [PCC], or defense mechanisms [PD]); in that way, she believed that no one would ever discover "the truth." Following the accident, although she was totally exonerated, her struggle concerned the fact that she was not in control, thus piercing her protective "mask" and revealing her core belief (CBT)/self-concept (PCC)/internal world (PD) that she "wasn't good enough."

So, whether you call them beliefs, self-concepts, or internal worlds, they amount to the same thing—they are the window through which we see the event in relation to ourselves and others, in terms of responsibility, safety, control or choice, and self-esteem. Without some form of intervention, they are usually accepted without question and can be resistant to change. Furthermore, it is not always possible to pinpoint the belief. For example, if the events that lead to the belief occurred when the child was preverbal, all the client's symptoms may be somatic. Ogden, Minton, and Pain (2006) propose that all levels of information processing, that is, cognitions, emotions, or somatic reactions, are viable targets for therapeutic intervention, and suggest that because each level is connected, by addressing one level, if therapy is effective, it should have an impact on the other levels. Consequently, by targeting the sensorimotor tendencies directly, this can lower emotional arousal and help shift beliefs.

FINDING THE ROOT OF THE PROBLEM

Schemas are often developed from childhood experiences, maintained and reinforced throughout life (Young, 1990). According to Janoff-Bulman, our earliest assumptions and representations generally have a far greater impact on our conceptual system than that which comes later. To fully understand the impact of later traumatic events, it is important

⊘ *Whatever You Do, Don't Do This...*

Never negate your client's experience or belief system.

Helen had been severely assaulted at school when she was 12. She recounted an incident when she was left bruised and bleeding and told by a teacher to sit in an empty classroom for an hour. Her therapist expressed surprise at this and suggested she had a distorted memory of the situation. This damaged the therapeutic relationship irrevocably.

Philips and Buncher (1999) proposed that as therapists, we have to take information on face value, because we only have the clients' word for whether their interpretation was real or imagined, true or false. However, they state that we can be certain that on that particular day, at that particular time, that person interpreted his thoughts in a certain way and from those thoughts a belief was created, a belief as to what that thought meant to him. They suggest that once an interpretation or belief has been given to a thought, it then becomes a reference point in the present tense, to enable the person to understand the world. At the same time, it becomes part of a structure that the unconscious mind will use to filter and sort all subsequent thoughts.

More important than the actual facts of Helen's experience was her interpretation of it.

to know what preceded it. The primacy effect similarly emphasizes the undue influence of early thoughts and beliefs (Bowlby, 1980).

Establishing the starting point of EMDR is an important concept and can determine the effectiveness (or otherwise!) of the therapy. Explaining the reasoning behind this approach raises issues for both clients and therapists, particularly if the client has come to therapy to deal with one particular issue, and you, as the therapist are suggesting that it may be more helpful to work on an earlier target memory. Consequently, it is important that the client understands the nature of traumatic memory, how belief systems develop over time, and how this may contribute to sensitizing an individual to current triggers. This can be done in a number of ways, and the following metaphors may be useful.

Pressure Cooker

It can be explained to the client that we all have an emotional "pressure cooker," which is filled with incidents throughout our life. However, if we continue filling up the pressure cooker and there is no emotional release valve, eventually, the pressure cooker will fill to the top and explode with an incident that may not normally have had a major impact. Therefore, it is important to make sure the pressure cooker is emptied by dealing with each incident in turn, starting with the ones at the bottom of the pot.

Gardening

Another simple way of explaining this to the client is by using the metaphor of the garden, by getting the client to imagine a large oak tree that has been growing for hundreds of years and the roots of which are damaging the foundation of the house. Chopping down the top of the tree would have no effect. However, if it were excavated from the roots, the foundations of the house could be stabilized. (It may help to draw this image.)

Pyramid

Memories and associated beliefs are built on each other over a lifetime. The strongest ones are formed in childhood and become the support for the rest of the pyramid. The bottom layers need to be the strongest to hold the upper layers in place securely. By removing shaky or unhelpful foundations, new, more adaptive ones can be created.

PREPARING FOR DESENSITIZATION

Choice of Dual Attention Stimulus

DAS can sound intrusive and induce anxiety in the client. Even after the therapists think that they have explained everything in a calm, clear manner, some clients have surprising questions, for example:

What exactly are you going to do to me?
Will I have electrodes on my head?
Will it hurt?
Is it like hypnosis?

It is important to allow the client the space and permission to ask these questions. Therapists should familiarize the client at an early stage with the mechanics of DAS and allow them some control in choosing the technique to be used. Although studies are ongoing as to whether EMs are more effective than other forms of DAS, some studies such as those of Andrade, Kavanagh, and Baddeley (1997), Kavanaugh, Freese, Andrade, and May (2001), Sharpley, Montgomery, and Scalzo (1996), and Van den Hout, Muris, Salemink, and Kindt (2001) have demonstrated that eye movements decrease the vividness of memory images and the associated emotion, suggesting that they may make a more effective contribution to treatment by decreasing the prominence of the memory and its associated affect.

Although on the initial EMDR training course manual eye movement and tapping are often the methods demonstrated, there is a wide range of DAS machines available. Therapists often feel more comfortable using these, because they minimize repetitive strain and therapist fatigue and allow some physical distance between client and therapist. If using a machine to induce eye movements, therapists need to position themselves so that they can monitor the client's tracking. Introducing a machine can add to the client's anxiety, and he/she should feel equally comfortable with whatever process is used. We also need to reiterate that the client is in control and this is *not* a passive process. This is particularly important if an individual has been subject to abuse. A word of warning if using technology: be prepared for the day that the machine refuses to cooperate!

Whichever method is used, there should be collaboration over issues such as speed of DAS, distance of focus for eye movements, or volume for sound. Avoid the windscreen wiper effect! If the client needs to remove glasses or contact lenses for desensitization using eye movements, therapists should be aware that this can invoke feelings of vulnerability and should be sensitive to this.

⊘ *Whatever You Do, Don't Do This...*

Catherine felt positive about her EMDR therapy up until the point where her male therapist demonstrated inducing DAS via tapping. He positioned his chair directly in front of her, knees touching, and proceeded to use his fingers to tap directly on Catherine's knees. This level of intimacy was very uncomfortable for her but, like many vulnerable clients, she felt unable to question the process and simply did not go back for further sessions.

If the therapist is not using a machine of some sort to deliver the DAS, the desensitization phase of EMDR can involve very close interpersonal proximity.

Always check the client's comfort with this close proximity. When using tapping on the back of a client's hands, therapists should always place some form of barrier between the clients' body and their hands, for example, a hard-backed book or cushion. This reduces any sensory connection traveling from the hands and onward.

Whichever method you choose, it is important to have another form of DAS and to prepare the client in advance for a potential change. This

---

Case Example
Preparing to Have a Change of DAS

Ursula always has a second method ready and prepares her client for a possible change.

"If we're starting with eye movements, I demonstrate how this would work and check out a comfortable distance, speed, and range. Then I let my client know that we have the option to change during desensitization and the possible reasons for this. I have a large hardcover book and I tell them that if we need to change I will pass them the book and ask them to put it across their knees with their hands on top. I show them how this would work and then demonstrate the tapping on the back of their hands. This means that if we do need to change we can do this with minimal interruption. This is especially important for clients when we are desensitizing abuse, and any unexpected movement or intrusion in their physical space could be scary. My clients also know they can ask for a change in DAS and that that's okay."

---

may be required, for example, if the client cannot focus on EM because of tears due to crying or tiredness. Some clients find it harder to retain a dual focus while watching lights or fingers and overly shift their attention to this external stimulus. Tapping or auditory stimulus can then become an option that is less distracting.

If you are using a machine, you should pay regard to your own positioning. You need to be able to monitor your client's nonverbal communication at the same time as being aware of the number of sets the machine is generating. With the traditional "ships passing" seating arrangement, the therapist can easily see the client's eyes moving from side to side. If a machine is promoting eye movements, you need to be able to check that the client is still retaining a dual focus and tracking the lights. Some machines will allow you to remotely control the duration and speed of DAS. Others will have a counter on the end of the light-bar displaying the number of DAS, and this is especially important for tactile and auditory stimulation where you may not have a clear indicator of numbers. Become familiar with the machine and, it may sound simple but, read the instructions and practice on a colleague.

Stop Signal

Where clients have issues over control, emphasize that EMDR uses the brain's natural healing and remind them of the anxiety management you have previously discussed and that they can control these symptoms and stop at any point. The client should be reminded of the stop signal before

> ### ⬩ *Common Pitfalls*
> ### *Working with Machines*
>
> "I was using headphones for auditory DAS and sitting across from my client. We started on the target image and I pressed the remote control. I was using a clock on the wall, the second hand, to give me an approximation of the number of DAS and when I stopped and asked the client what they noticed, they told me nothing had changed. After a couple more sets like this, my client asked whether they were supposed to be able to hear the beeps from the headphones. The remote control had stopped working and my client had been sitting there in silence and trusting I knew what I was doing!"

each desensitization session. When choosing a stop signal, be clear about its nature. Having a verbal command "stop" may cause problems where the client is verbalizing an aspect of his or her memory, for example, telling a perpetrator to stop. Similarly, holding up both hands may be an articulation of trying to "push the trauma/perpetrator away." A single hand held up is the most common signal. There is a fine line between encouraging the client to maintain control of the process by stopping and allowing distress to peak and fall away naturally. This is where the therapeutic relationship and good preparation pay off. The client should feel able and supported in managing strong emotions yet empowered to stop if they feel in danger of being overwhelmed. A common metaphor is that of going through a dark tunnel—when things are at their blackest and scariest, that's the time to motor on through.

Providing Clear Instructions

Before starting DAS focusing on the target memory, it is important to give clear instructions to the client so as to provide as safe an experience as possible and address any performance anxiety. By this stage, you will have already introduced the concept of EMDR to the client.

> ### Case Example
> ### Word Association Game
>
> Carol sometimes uses this metaphor, finding that it helps clients not to censor seemingly irrelevant material that surfaces.
>
> "Have you ever played the word association game—you know where a group of people start with one word and the next person has to say the first thing that comes into his or her head, then the next person responds to that one, very quickly and without consciously thinking about the link? And sometimes someone says something really bizarre and you think 'where did that come from?'
>
> Well, desensitization can be like that sometimes. You may start with a particular target memory and your mind takes you to bizarre or unrelated memories. It's important just to notice where it's going and let me know. Try not to judge or censor the memory as it doesn't have to make sense. Just go with the flow. Trust that your mind will take you where it needs to go but sometimes it's like a magical mystery tour."

It is important to repeat this and give more detail about the potential client experience. As stated earlier, clients may have forgotten the original information or have remembered it in a distorted way. Later problems can often be side-stepped by ensuring that a client has the best possible understanding of what desensitization entails and what feedback you require. However, no matter how well the therapist explains this, there will be times that the client does not take on board the information.

A variety of explanations can be given and repeated. Chapter Resource 4.1 shows an example script of how to explain what will happen in the session.

As previously discussed, many people use metaphors to understand processes, and they may automatically produce their own, which you can adapt to the EMDR process.

It can be hard to explain desensitization without setting client expectation. Here is another way of doing it:

At the beginning, we will start with thinking about a particular aspect of your target memory. That will involve the image that represents the worst part of the memory, a negative thought and the accompanying emotions and physical sensations. Once we start the eye movements (or other DAS), you may notice changes. This may be that the image changes or disappears or you remember different aspects of the incident. Sometimes it is the emotion that changes—it may intensify or decrease or change, for example, from fear to sadness. You may notice new thoughts of different times in your life; other memories may surface. The physical sensations may change, for example, if you start with a headache, you may find this increases or reduces or changes location. The important thing to remember is that you cannot get this wrong. All you need to do is notice what is changing and tell me what you notice when I have stopped the eye movements. For some people, there will be a stream of fragmented images, thoughts, emotions, and physical sensations, for others the changes will be more subtle and we will have to look closely for what is changing. Everybody's experience will be slightly different and there is no right way for you to do this. Your brain will heal naturally in its own way.

Because desensitization the first time is such an unknown for clients, they can suffer from performance anxiety. No matter how well you think you have prepared your clients, they may have unexpressed fears about the actual desensitization:

What if I can't do it properly?

Will it change me?
Will I be aware of what's going on?
Will it make me go mad?

Case Example
The Hot Seat

I give my clients the option to use a third chair in my consulting room for the actual desensitization part of sessions. My clients call this the Hot Seat and the majority prefer to use this.

We spend the first part of a desensitization session refining the target memory and associated NCs and so on. Then they move to the Hot Seat. Once we have reprocessed the memory (complete or not) they return to their original chair for a debriefing and relaxation exercise. My clients say it helps them to separate from what can be the hardest part of the session and to consider their experience objectively. They feel safer in their own chairs before desensitization and more relaxed in it afterward. The Hot Seat contains the experience and can be left behind.

❧ Common Pitfall
Client Performance Anxiety

One way that clients can demonstrate their performance anxiety is by subtly preventing a desensitization session from ever happening. Simon found that his client Nick would suddenly have other issues to discuss when they had preplanned a session for desensitization. Nick would want to talk about everything under the sun and Simon would struggle to maintain a focus to these sessions before time ran out. This became a pattern that was eventually picked up in supervision. Simon's supervisor suggested he gently confront Nick, stating that he had noticed a pattern and asking whether this something to do with any fears that he had about going ahead with the desensitization.

By doing this and addressing the emerging anxiety of which Nick had felt ashamed, they could move on and the actual desensitization although successful was seen by Nick as an anticlimax compared with what he had been imagining!

It is important to be aware of this and preempt questions as much as possible. Remind your client that there are no stupid questions, and if they have any worries at all they should express them. If you sense they are at all reluctant, explore this with them.

Metaphors for Managing High Affect

One of the most common fears for clients is whether they will be able to handle any strong emotions that arise.

Train

It can be helpful to compare the experience of memory processing with EMDR to being on a train journey. Ask the client to think about sitting on a train looking out of the window, and second by second the scenery changes. Sometimes the view will be colorful, sometimes it will be barren, certain things may stand out, you may see things you do not expect, but it always changes. EMDR desensitization is a similar process to this, with the images, thoughts, and sensations changing very quickly.

Video

Another way of helping the client to understand the way EMDR helps to process memories is the metaphor of a video. You can get them to imagine that they are watching the events unfold as if they were watching a film of the event. This also allows the clients to remove themselves slightly from the processing, particularly if the memory is eliciting high affect.

The Splinter

And finally, one of the ways to help clients manage and understand the strong emotions that may be experienced in EMDR desensitization is that of the splinter. Ask clients to imagine what would happen if they had a splinter in their finger and they chose to leave it there. Eventually it would become very sore and infected because it is not meant to be there, a bit like a traumatic memory. As such, EMDR is a metaphorical way of removing the splinter, which, initially, may hurt, however, as the splinter is cleaned out, it is allowed to heal so that when you touch it, it does not hurt anymore.

NEGATIVE COGNITIONS AND THE TARGET MEMORY

In choosing the target memory, therefore, the therapist and client need to determine the touchstone event, that is, the earliest memory linked to the current pathology.

As you will have learned on your EMDR training course, the NC

- Should be in the present tense
- Should be a statement about the self
- Should be relevant to the current situation *and* the past event(s) to be targeted
- Is generalizable
- Produces affect that resonates with the target image.

Establishing the NC is an important aspect of the target memory, and it is probably the issue that is raised the most by novice (and experienced!)

Case Example
Socratic Questioning

Presenting condition: Generalized anxiety

Target memory: Bullying incident at school

Therapist: What are the negative words that go best with that image?

Client: I should have run away.

Therapist: Because you didn't run away, what does that say about you?

Client: I got it wrong.

Therapist: What happens when you get it wrong?

Client: I get hurt.

Therapist: What does that say about you?

Client: I can't protect myself.

Therapist: What does that mean for you?

Final statement = I am in danger.

therapists. And, just to complicate matters, there may be more than one NC associated with an event.

From the moment the client walks into the room, therapists can be tuning their NC antennae and listening for examples of statements that lead to core beliefs, for example,

"That never works for me"
"I was always the stupid one"
"People always leave me"
"I always get it wrong"
"Something bad always happens."

These can give the therapist an indication of potential core beliefs that can be later refined into an NC.

Statements can be converted into a core belief using methods such as Socratic questioning. The NC should be as powerful as possible, that is, a behavioral statement such as "I should have done something" is not as powerful as a characterological statement such as "I am weak."

Depending on your terminology, predisposing factors are another way of determining threads or themes through the client's life.

Using another gardening metaphor, the NC can be considered as a weed running through various life events. If the top of the weed is removed, the person may feel some relief because the weed appears to have gone. However, if the roots remain the weed will keep coming back time after time. By locating the roots (that is, the origins of the NC) and removing (targeting) them, the rest of the plant will shrivel and die.

Case Example 1
Negative Cognition

Harry was involved in a road traffic accident involving multiple fatalities. His NC was "I'm in danger."

From his timeline, earlier events with this same NC were identified—an incident when he had nearly drowned at the age of 11, serious bullying, and a near miss as a schoolboy pedestrian with a bus.

His therapist began desensitization with the earliest incident in this thread.

Case Example 2
Negative Cognition

Misplaced feelings of shame and isolation accompanied Paul's NC of "I should have done something. It's my fault" when he considered the suicide of his colleague.

This mirrored feelings he had when at school. He had struggled in class while dealing with the break up of his parents' marriage. He felt responsible for not being able to prevent their ultimate divorce.

Occasionally earlier memories are unclear, or the client is not aware of the memories that may be "feeding" the current issue. These can sometimes be identified by asking the client to do a lifeline, which can help the client and the therapist recognize patterns or themes; alternatively, the floatback technique can be used.

Floatback

As you will have discovered on your training course, the floatback technique is a way of eliciting an earlier memory if the client is having difficulty processing a current memory (Shapiro, 2001). It may be that the SUDS are not reducing despite the desensitization process, or the client does not know when the current difficulty first started. Depending on the particular scenario, you will either already have or will need to elicit the image, NC, and so on of the current situation, and this particular technique then allows the client to literally "float back" to the earliest

---

Case Example 3
Negative Cognition

Sarah was involved in a road traffic accident and was left with an ongoing, slight disability. Her NC was "I can't protect myself."

Using a floatback technique, Sarah recalled earlier events including a street robbery and earlier domestic violence with this same NC.

---

memory he/she has that involves the same thread. You will then process the earliest memory in the normal way.

If the client is having difficulty providing an NC despite all the above techniques, another method to use is to connect the client to the body sensations that they get when they think of the memory. Then ask them to imagine it as a shape and a color; once you have that image, ask, "if it had a voice what would it be saying?" This may enable you to pick up on the theme of the belief and then use the downward arrow technique or Socratic questioning to pinpoint the NC. Once again, it is about using techniques that you are already aware of and integrating them into the EMDR protocol.

⤷ *Common Pitfall*
Client Does Not Mention a Significant Earlier Event

Angela was a survivor of the 2004 Asian Tsunami and had witnessed loss and devastation on a grand scale. During history taking, she reported a generally happy childhood and no significant previous events.

Her therapist proceeded with desensitization of the worst part of the disaster. The image was of a mother pleading with Angela to help her find her child. The NC was "I am helpless," and the emotions were anxiety, grief, and guilt. Despite initial reduction in Subjective Units of Disturbance Scale (SUDS), Angela made little progress. At this stage, her therapist decided to use the floatback technique on the NC and related emotions.

Angela immediately went to the memory of her baby brother's cot death and her mother sobbing hysterically on finding him. Angela was 6 at the time and had been jealous of the new baby. She had not revealed this event to her therapist because it still provoked guilt and she chose to avoid this. It had become a taboo subject.

Having explored the potential significance of the baby's death, Angela and her therapist agreed to target the earlier trauma. The desensitization of the first incident led to a later successful completion of the Tsunami trauma.

Sometimes clients take longer to build up the rapport and to begin to work collaboratively with their therapist. For a very few clients, it is only when they have experienced a desensitization session that they are able to open up and share additional information. This can have an impact on the case conceptualization.

Case Example
Using the Floatback Technique

Kate had been diagnosed with PTSD following a very difficult birth leading to an emergency cesarian section. With her therapist Sarah they had begun the assessment phase on the target memory of the delivery room being suddenly filled with medical staff and Kate's panic. Her worst image was of the delivery room door banging open and what seemed like dozens of people charging into the room.

Sarah: So now Kate, I want you to bring up the delivery room door banging open, the negative words "I am in danger," and just notice what feelings are coming up for you, where you are feeling them in your body...and then let your mind float back to an earlier time in your life...perhaps when you were a child or adolescent...don't deliberately search for anything...just let your mind float back and trust that it will take you to where it needs to go. It might be a big or a small memory...don't prejudge it...just tell me the first scene that comes to mind where you had similar thoughts of being in danger and feelings of fear and panic.

Kate: I've gone to when I was about...I don't know, about 5 or 6 years old. I'm in the kitchen with my mum...we're about to have our tea and my dad's just come home. He's really mad...I think he'd been drinking again. He's swung the kitchen door so hard it nearly came off its hinges. I was terrified. It still makes me anxious now thinking about that.

Sarah: What picture represents the worst part of that incident to you now?

Kate: The violence of him slamming into the room and the panic in my mum's face.

Sarah: And what words go best with that picture to express your negative belief about yourself now?

Kate: I'm not safe—something bad is going to happen.

Sarah: When you bring up that picture of your dad slamming into the room, what would you like to believe about yourself now?

Kate: That he can't hurt me or my mum anymore. That it's over.

Sarah: And how true does that statement feel to you now on a scale of 1 to 7, where 1 feels completely false and 7 feels completely true?

(continued)

> ## *Case Example*
> ## *Using the Floatback Technique (continued)*
>
> **Kate:** I know it's completely true but I still feel it's not...it feels like a 1 or a 2.
>
> **Sarah:** So when you bring up that picture of your dad slamming into the room and the words "I'm not safe," what emotion(s) do you feel now?
>
> **Kate:** Scared, like butterflies in my stomach and sweaty palms...my head's gone a bit fuzzy as well (physical sensations given along with emotions).
>
> **Sarah:** And on the scale of 0 to 10, where 0 is no disturbance or neutral and 10 is the highest disturbance you can imagine...
>
> **Kate:** It's a 9!
>
> Sarah and Kate proceeded with desensitization of the childhood event prior to targeting the childbirth trauma. This was reprocessed in a subsequent session to good effect but Kate also gained a good deal of insight into reasons why this later event had been particularly distressing for her.
>
> *Note:* For this client, the floatback elicited the earliest memory related to the current issue, however, for other clients, there may be more than one floatback required to get to the root of the problem.

COMPLETING THE BASELINE ASSESSMENT

So by this stage, you are fairly confident that you have identified the appropriate target memory and its related NC. Many practitioners find it useful to use the structured worksheet provided on most training courses. This leads the practitioner and client through the important assessment factors and further clarifies the target memory as well as its effects on the client in the present when thinking about it.

Image

Visual imagery is often a significant feature of the traumatic memory and is usually associated with powerful emotions. The client should be asked which image represents the worst part of the memory. You can ask for this in various ways, for example:

What picture represents the worst part?
If you took a snapshot of the worst part of what happened, what would it show?
If you could get rid of one image of the incident, what would it be?
If you could store it away in a box, what would the label look like?
(For a video) If you were to freeze frame at the worst part, what would you see?

Sometimes clients will give detailed descriptions. They may be associated within the image or not, that is, they may be seeing themselves through their own eyes or as a bystander. If a client is strongly associated with a vivid image and is finding this overwhelming, the therapist can help him/her stand back a little by a distancing technique such as watching it on a video that can be remote controlled.

Conversely, some people are not very visual and may struggle to come up with an image. Some may find it hard to connect emotionally to a memory and the therapist needs to ensure that the memory is as vivid as possible for those with little affect or disproportionately low SUDS. Questions such as how does she look and what does she see can be helpful in these cases to get the client to strengthen the image.

Occasionally clients are genuinely unable to come up with an image. It is worth checking out their general visualization ability, for example, asking them to picture their front door. If they can do that, there could

---

Case Example
The Image

Judith's client was very organized and methodical but struggled to articulate the image. Judith used the following metaphor.

"If you were to put this memory in a storage box in the loft with a representative snapshot photograph on the front, what would that photograph show? Can you think of an appropriate caption or label that would also go on the front of the box?"

Case Example
Distressing Images

Harry witnessed his brother's death by hanging. The image of his brother's distorted face was permeating every aspect of Harry's life, intruding during the day and coming to him in nightmares. Distancing techniques were not providing much relief for this.

Although Phase 2 deals with symptom management, some clients, such as Harry, will still be managing distressing symptoms before desensitization Therefore it is important to acknowledge this with the client.

It was important that Harry was given hope that EMDR could help with the image, particularly during the preparation and history-taking sessions. Harry needed to know that there was light at the end of the tunnel for such intrusive and distressing symptoms. However, there is also a line to tread between offering false hope and reassuring the client.

---

be an avoidance issue. It is important to be aware of this but not to labor the point.

However, if you find you are consistently not getting an image (or another component for desensitization), you need to consider

- Are you asking the client in the right way?
- Are you avoiding asking about particular components, for example, emotions—because you find dealing with strong emotions difficult?
- Are you rushing the assessment and not spending sufficient time exploring the more elusive components?

And finally, remember that the image may not be the one that you have conjured up!

Positive Cognition

EMDR does not just desensitize a memory but links it to more adaptive knowledge. Speaking metaphorically, the memory was previously stored in a box marked with an NC such as "I'm in danger" and, once

---

◯ ***Whatever You Do, Don't Do This…***

Roger's client was unable to provide an image for desensitization after a boating accident. Roger spent a full session trying to elicit the image while his client felt increasingly under pressure. He told his client that without the image they could not proceed with desensitization.

Unsurprisingly, his client dropped out of therapy believing he was a failure.

---

processed, is moved to a different box that needs a new label such as "I'm safe, it's over."

The positive cognition should be:

- Stated in the present tense
- Appropriate and true, avoiding unrealistic statements
- Empowering
- A statement about the self.

PCs to avoid include:

- Always/never statements such as "I am always in control." They are generally unrealistic and unachievable
- Statements such as "It never happened." EMDR is not able to remove the reality of what happened
- Statements where other people have influence, such as "I can make them love me"
- Fundamentally flawed PCs such as "I'm not going to die."

Occasionally, the client will provide a PC that is seemingly unrelated to the NC. Examples of this include:

NC: I should have done more; PC: I am safe now
NC: I am vulnerable; PC: It wasn't my fault
NC: I can't cope; PC: I am getting better
NC: I am helpless; PC: I have to accept this

Case Example
Positive Cognition

Karen had experienced literacy problems at school due to her undiagnosed dyslexia. As an adult, she had very low self-esteem and difficulties standing up for herself. One particularly troubling memory was of a teacher humiliating her in front of the class. Her NC was "I am stupid," and her initial PC was "I am not stupid."

As this was a negatively framed statement, her therapist helped her to choose a more appropriate one stated in the positive which was "I am intelligent."

In Karen's case, this was an appropriate PC because she could see evidence of her many achievements despite her dyslexia.

However, the PC should be acceptable to the client, who may not be capable of being very positive at this stage. In the similar case of Gillian, she recoiled from the idea of being intelligent. The initial PC was "I am good enough," which was more comfortable to her.

Therapists should remember that the PC may change and evolve after desensitization and will be reconsidered prior to installation.

If you consider that the beliefs are categorized in terms of safety, responsibility, control, choice, and esteem, then there appears to be a mismatch above. It could be that the PC is wrong, *but* it could be that the NC is not reaching the heart of the matter. This could be because there is a fear of verbalizing it. In the above instance, the PC suggests that there is an underlying NC of "I am not safe" and this should be checked out with the client.

Validity of Cognition Self-Report Scale

On occasions, the client will talk about a memory that evokes a great deal of emotion, and the client states a high level of SUDS, however, when the VOC is checked around the positive belief, in connection with the event, it appears that the numbers do not add up. The therapist should ensure that the VOC is being measured emotionally rather than intellectually and is being directly related to the target.

⊘ *Whatever You Do, Don't Do This...*

Sue had been for a girls' night out and, having had two bottles of wine, had decided to drive the short distance home. Unfortunately, she was involved in a collision with a pedestrian who was left confined to a wheelchair.

Sue suffered intense guilt, intrusive images relating to the accident, and nightmares. In the assessment phase prior to desensitization, Sue's NC was "It's my fault" but she could not come up with a suitable PC. Her therapist strongly suggested "It's not my fault" as the PC.

This was not ecologically valid, and Sue felt very uncomfortable with the concept that she was not to blame. She felt this was unrealistic and almost immoral to be aspiring to believe this. Consequently, the therapeutic relationship was undermined.

A better PC may have been "I can learn from this."

Alternatively, if this still did not change, the NC and PC may need to be explored a little more in depth.

Emotions

Clients can become confused with making the distinction between thoughts and feelings; in such a case, again use the methods previously mentioned to elicit the feelings from the thoughts. In addition, it can be difficult for clients to connect to their emotions, particularly if this is an incident that has been buried for a long time. However, as previously mentioned, it is important to ensure that the client can manage strong affect prior to desensitization, because EMDR can sometimes elicit powerful emotions quite quickly; consequently, the client must be prepared for this.

Subjective Units of Disturbance Scale

The SUDS should reflect the client's evaluation of the total disturbance. If a client suggests SUDS of 10, this leaves no room for maneuver if the level of distress increases as DAS starts. Therefore, it may be appropriate to ask on a scale of 1–100.

Case Example
Validation of Cognition

Mary had presented an early target memory of a childhood incident with a SUDS level of 8 and her NC was "I am a bad person." In determining the positive cognition, Mary said she would like to believe, "I am a good person"; however, when the therapist asked how much she believed that statement in connection to the incident now, she felt it was 6/7. This did not "match" the SUDS, therefore the therapist explored the mismatch in a little more detail and it emerged that, although logically she felt she was a good person, "deep down" she doubted it. The VOC was then rerated on the part of her that doubted the statement and it was down to 3/7. This enabled the client to align her thinking and feeling.

➤ Common Pitfall
Working in the Dark

Depending on your client's history, and the presenting issue, you may find that some clients do not actually want to talk through the incident. However, without forcing clients it is important to let them know that this is a journey you are going to be taking with them and sometimes it can help to talk it through so that when they are going into "dark places" you can be alongside them. This can be particularly important if the client has been told "never to speak about what has happened" or when they have told someone, they were not believed, or they have minimized the impact of the incident.

One of the advantages of EMDR is that the therapist does not have to know all the intimate details but equally, the therapist needs a rough map of the terrain. This needs careful balancing. If a client gets stuck and you do not know the elements of his or her story, it may be difficult to intervene appropriately.

Alternatively, SUDS may start off relatively low, even though the incident is a defining moment in the client's life. However, it is important to point out that this may increase initially when desensitization begins.

If SUDS is very low, for example, 5 and below, it may be prudent to clarify whether this is the correct target memory or if the client is dissociating from, avoiding, or not tuned into his or her emotions.

Physical Sensations

If the clients' NC is around safety, they may be expected to report anxious physical symptoms, for example, racing heart and sweating palms. Sometimes the physical symptoms are sensory such as smells or tastes. Furthermore, the client may feel pain in parts of the body that were hurt in the incident. It is important to watch for signs of dissociation, as previously discussed, if the physical sensations become overwhelming. Ensuring that the client is aware of your presence and of being in the room can be enough to keep the client grounded, with one foot in the present and one in the past.

Does It All Fit Together?

Before you proceed with the desensitization, just make a final check on whether it all fits together, we have included an example of a well-completed worksheet (Shapiro, 2001) and one that has some room for improvement with comments as to why!

CLIENT: John DATE: Jan 8	CLIENT: John DATE: Jan 8
Presenting issue or memory:	**Presenting issue or memory:**
What issue or memory would you like to work on today?	What issue or memory would you like to work on today?
The head-on collision I was involved in	The head-on collision I was involved in
Picture:	**Picture:**
What picture represents the worst part of that incident to you now?	What picture represents the worst part of that incident to you now?
The headlights coming toward me	I'm driving round the bend, coming over the hill and there's a car coming straight at me.
	This is too wordy and imprecise. It doesn't get to the actual hot spot of the trauma.
NC:	**NC:**
What words go best with that picture that express your negative belief about yourself now?	What words go best with that picture that express your negative belief about yourself now?
I am not safe	I'm frightened.
	This is not a statement reflecting a self-belief.

(*continued*)

Positive cognition (PC):
When you bring up that picture, what
would you like to believe about yourself now?
It's over.

VOC:
As you bring up that picture, how true
does that statement (PC) feel to you
now on a scale of 1 to 7, where 1 feels
completely false and 7 feels completely
true?

1 **2** 3 4 5 6 7

Emotions/feelings:
When you bring up that picture of the
headlights coming toward you, and
those words I am not safe, what
emotion(s) do you feel now?
Fear, a bit of anger too

SUD:
On a scale of 0 to 10, where 0 is no
disturbance or neutral and 10 is the
highest disturbance you can imagine,
how disturbing does the incident/
memory feel to you now?

0 1 2 3 4 5 6 7 **8** 9 10

Location of body sensation(s):
Where do you feel it in your body?
Tight chest, sweaty palms, feel sick

Positive cognition (PC):
When you bring up that picture, what would
you like to believe about yourself now?
I'm going to be safe to drive.
*This is not a self-evaluation, and probably not
realistic.*

VOC:
As you bring up that picture, how true does
that statement (PC) feel to you now on a
scale of 1 to 7, where 1 feels completely
false and 7 feels completely true?

1 **2** 3 4 5 6 7

Emotions/feelings:
When you bring up that picture of you driving
round the bend, coming over the hill and a car
coming straight at you, and those words I'm
frightened, what emotion(s) do you feel now?
I think he could have killed me, and my children would have been left without a dad.
*These are not emotions but do hint at beliefs
and feelings; so they should be explored.*

SUD:
On a scale of 0 to 10, where 0 is no disturbance or neutral and 10 is the highest disturbance you can imagine, how disturbing
does the incident/memory feel to you now?

0 1 2 3 4 5 6 7 **8** 9 10

Location of body sensation(s):
Where do you feel it in your body?
In my head.
*What is happening? For example, dizziness,
lightheadedness, headaches.*

Working With Different Levels of Awareness and Articulation

Obviously we work with clients who have varying abilities and different
learning styles, and some can be more self-aware than others. All these
factors need to be taken into account when drawing the information for
the desensitization. Sometimes a client may mix up the different factors,
for example, when asked how they are feeling, they may tell you what

they are thinking. It is important not to encourage feelings of failure. Therefore, use the information they give you to complete the worksheet in the order they provide it.

CASE STUDY: EMMA'S ASSESSMENT PHASE

Emma agrees that it would be useful to begin with the memory of her mother shouting at her and her brother James. She likes the "weed" metaphor and feels that her relationship with her mother has never been as relaxed as she would hope. Even now, she seeks her approval and believes this is one of her drivers to "be good" and work hard.

The memory is very vivid and this gives me confidence that we are dealing with an important event.

Therapist: When you think about that event, what is the worst part for you?

Emma: Mother crying and shouting, I've never seen her so mad. She's shaking with it but she's really upset too. I don't think I'd ever seen her cry before. And James and I are just standing there not knowing what to do.

Therapist: And what words best go with this picture?

Emma: I wish she wasn't so angry.

Therapist: How does that make you feel about yourself?

Emma: It's my fault.

Therapist: If you wanted to be able to look back on that memory with a more positive belief about yourself, what would that be?

Emma: I guess that it wasn't my fault. I was only a child.

Therapist: And when you think about that image and the thought that "it wasn't my fault," how true does that feel to you right now? If you could rate it on a scale out of 7 where 1/7 is completely false and 7/7 is completely true.

Emma: Well, I was only a child. That bit's completely true.

Therapist: Rate it on how you feel, rather than what you rationally know. There's often a mismatch.

Emma: You're right. I do feel guilty. Thinking that it's not my fault just doesn't fit right. I'd rate it about 2/7.

Therapist: So, if you think about that image of your mum being really upset and the thought that "it's my fault," what emotions come up for you right now?

Emma: I still feel a bit scared—I don't like conflict—and ashamed, guilty—like it's my fault—and I feel sad for my mother.

Therapist: If you were to give these feelings a rating, say out of 10, where 0/10 is no disturbance and 10/10 is the worse you could feel, what would you score right now?

Emma: I'd give it an 8/10. It's crazy really. It was a long time ago, but thinking about it now still really upsets me.

Therapist: And if you scan up and down your body for tension or unusual sensations, what do you notice?

Emma: I feel a bit sickly, butterflies in my stomach and this kind of heat rising up my neck ... I feel like I'm blushing and hot.

FREQUENTLY ASKED QUESTIONS

Q: **What should I do if my client begins to abreact during the assessment session?**

A: Completing the worksheet will naturally cause a rise in disturbance. By now, if you have followed the protocol, your client is prepared for desensitization, has coping strategies, a safe place, and a good therapeutic relationship, and understands the process and the stop signal, so begin desensitization. However, if you feel that your clients are becoming overwhelmed and not actually processing, you need to ground them, return to some stability, and possibly take them to their safe place. In that instance, you may need to use distancing techniques or return to exploring coping strategies and the client's ability to manage strong emotions. The priority is that both you and your client feel safe within the process.

Q: **My client was involved in an incident during which she nearly died. Her image is not of the incident but of her family standing around her graveside having buried her. This is the most distressing part for her. She has a less disturbing memory of the actual incident. Which should I target?**

A: Often clients will have imagined images and scenarios that are highly distressing. The imagined image is the client's interpretation of her experience, representing the worst part, and as such should be targeted in the usual way.

Q: **I find it very difficult to determine the NCs. Is it okay to just give the client the list of PCs and NCs?**

A: As a last resort, this can be done but it has its drawbacks. First, the client can identify with multiple statements and become further demoralized. Let's face it, on a bad day, many therapists would do the same! Second, it may become less of a last resort and more of a routine. Third, it may not be as effective as drawing out the NC from the client. During that collaborative process, the client is making sense of his or her thoughts and feelings. It is also an important time for the therapist to gain and demonstrate a deeper understanding of the client.

LEARNING SUMMARY

You should feel confident that you are able to:

- Help the client to establish the root of the problem using various metaphors to explain the process
- Ensure the client has identified the correct NC for the target memory
- If appropriate, use the floatback technique to ensure the earliest memory is being targeted
- Complete the baseline assessment ensuring it all fits together

RESOURCES

4.1: Example Script

"EMDR processing is different to talking therapy, in that we will spend a few minutes processing the memory and then I will stop you, at that point you will be asked to feedback a snapshot of the strongest aspect of the memory that is going on at that moment—it may be an image, thought, feeling, or sensation—and then you will be asked to continue. Throughout the processing phase of EMDR, I will be encouraging you. It isn't important that you hear what I am saying. You just need to be aware that even though you are remembering an unpleasant incident, you are safe here with me and nobody can hurt you when you are in this room. (Talk about the stop signal, but use the metaphor of getting through a dark tunnel.)"

5 Opening Pandora's Box

By this stage, the therapist should feel reasonably confident that he or she has laid the foundations for a good therapeutic relationship and selected the appropriate target memory with all its associated components and that both therapist and client are ready to begin processing. This chapter focuses on the desensitization phase during which the therapist processes the dysfunctional material. It will explore a range of issues that are frequently raised in this phase, including therapist anxiety and abreactions. The chapter looks at challenges during the desensitization phase, such as blocked processing and the use of cognitive interweaves.

THERAPIST ANXIETY

It is not only the client who gets anxious about the desensitization phase. It can be very daunting to the new EMDR practitioner. Performance anxiety can be a block for the therapist as well as for the client. Common saboteurs include:

- I need more training before I start
- I am too afraid I will make the client worse
- What if I cannot do it?
- What if the desensitization harms my client?
- What if I open up something that I cannot close again?

- What if it does not work and the client thinks I am not very good?
- Where do I look when my client is using DAS? It feels intrusive to be monitoring closely when I am not engaged in conversation
- Will I look stupid waving my fingers about?

The key to managing these anxieties is to be clear about your role. The therapists' role is distinct in this phase and involves supporting the client verbally with minimum intervention unless the client is stuck. They should help the client to focus on the flow of feelings, thoughts, and body sensations as they unfold. The therapist will observe the nonverbal signs, troughs and peaks of sensations, and will monitor the changes. The therapist also needs to help the client to maintain duality, keeping the client grounded and connected to the present.

It can be very tempting to analyze, predict, judge, or interpret surfacing material. However, as long as the client is processing, which at times can feel like being on a magical mystery tour, a more adaptive process will be facilitated if you have faith and go with the flow. Ensuring the client is aware of how this phase progresses and why can normalize this process and reduce both client's and therapist's anxiety.

Case Example
The Self-Conscious Therapist

Nicky accepts that DAS can look odd but still prefers the old-fashioned way to using a machine.

"There can be an element of feeling self-conscious during desensitization. At first, I used to feel rather daft. I even considered getting a machine but that felt too technical and as though it may be an obstacle in the room. Now I tend to be up front about the silliness of the desensitization and tell clients it can seem odd but hey, if it works! I remember one client telling me at the end of a session that he had had an image of me waving at him like a member of the Royal Family. In his case, it was a sign of his mood lifting and coming back to the here and now fully and we both laughed at the metaphor. I think it's about being relaxed with the process and trusting it works."

> ### ⭐ *Common Pitfall*
> ### *Feeling Redundant*
>
> A common feeling among novice EMDR therapists is that of being redundant. As Jason says "When I first started using EMDR, I felt I should be doing something during desensitization. I actually felt redundant and disempowered and it was so tempting to intervene. Sometimes my client would say something that I really wanted to explore or challenge, and it was frustrating sitting back and saying to just notice that. I have to admit sometimes I did stop desensitization and explore things that had arisen. What changed me was when a more experienced colleague asked whether this wasn't just a bit arrogant—thinking I had more to contribute by saying something rather than letting the person's brain naturally heal itself. I suppose it's about learning to trust the process and also about acknowledging my skills in other aspects of the EMDR therapy such as all the other phases. Now, I can let Phase 4 take care of itself mostly unless I really do need to intervene, say with a cognitive interweave."

DESENSITIZATION

It is important at the start of the desensitization session that the therapist reiterates what will happen and reminds clients about the stop signal, the option to change method of DAS, and their safe place. Clients should be reassured that they are in control of the process and can stop if they feel they are becoming overwhelmed or tired, but also reminded that they have the inner resources and the therapist's support to manage strong affect if needed.

In terms of the AIP model, the target for processing can be considered as a node, "a pivotal place among the physiologically associated material" (Shapiro, 2001, p. 34). This node will have channels where associated thoughts, images, emotions, memories, and physical sensations are stored. Because we do not know what each individual's memory network is made up of, it is not possible to predict precisely what will surface during desensitization. Therefore, it can be difficult to explain the client's potential experience of desensitization without setting expectations that are rigid. Here is one example of how to prepare the client, but it is important to develop your own "script" and practice saying it aloud or to a colleague or supervisor.

"At the beginning of desensitization, I will help you to start thinking about a particular aspect of your target memory. That will involve the image that represents the worst part of the memory, a negative thought, and the accompanying emotions and physical sensations. Once we start the desensitization, you may notice changes. This may be that the image changes or disappears or you remember different aspects of the incident. Sometimes it is the emotion that changes—it may intensify or decrease or change, for example, from fear to sadness. You may notice new thoughts about the target memory or about different times in your life—other memories may surface. The physical sensations may change, for example, if you start with a headache, you may find this increases or reduces or changes location. The important thing to remember is that you can't get this wrong. All you need to do is just notice what is changing and tell me what you notice when I have stopped the desensitization. Don't discard any information that might come up, even if it doesn't seem relevant. For some people there will be a stream of fragmented images, thoughts, emotions, and physical sensations; for others the changes will be more subtle and we will have to look closely to see what is changing. Everybody's experience will be slightly different and there is no right or wrong way for you to do this. Your brain will heal naturally in its own way."

Once DAS has started, the client should begin to process the dysfunctional material. As stated earlier, memories are linked to channels of association and, as the client processes the memory, he or she will move down each channel. To completely process a memory, all channels need to be cleared. The therapist will not know how many channels there are.

❧ *Common Pitfall*
Misunderstanding What Will Happen

How you explain the desensitization can be easily misunderstood. For example, if you begin by asking clients to "hold the image" or "run the video" and then begin DAS, clients may assume that

The image is the most central part of this and they must concentrate on imagery, dismissing emotions, body sensations, thoughts, arising memories, or

They must keep the image in mind and if it fades or is replaced then they are not doing things right.

⊘ *Whatever You Do, Don't Do This...*

Harry was not sure how often he was supposed to check SUDS and fell into the habit of asking at the end of every set of eye movements. After some time of doing this he began to notice he was becoming more frustrated with his EMDR clients than his other clients and finally discussed this in supervision. He realized that when the SUDS did not reduce quickly, he felt he was doing something wrong and panicked when SUDS increased. He realized he was creating performance anxiety for himself and for his clients, and he suspected some were even misreporting in an attempt to please him. He was overemphasizing the importance of the SUDS and potentially missing other material that was arising during desensitization.

When the client indicates no change and that he or she is feeling relatively comfortable or neutral, the therapist can assume that channel has cleared. The therapist will then return the client's attention to the original target checking for disturbance and, where present, continuing DAS. Once a memory is fully processed, the client may be unable to access the original image and should simply be asked to think about it.

Not every desensitization session will be complete. Chapter 6 discusses how to manage incomplete sessions and Phases 5–8.

ABREACTIONS

High levels of distress, or abreactions, can be common during desensitization.

This may be emotional or physical, and clients will vary in their abilities to manage this. Despite good preparation, clients can still be surprised by their level of response during desensitization.

As well as the obviously distressed client, there may be other more subtle indications that a client is experiencing strong affect. Therapists need to be alert to the signs of hyperarousal, such as accelerated heart rate and respiration, sweating, or skin becoming pale or grey, in their clients. Some clients may report a feeling that they may vomit or even have a bowel movement. This could be a current manifestation of high anxiety or a somatic memory. Either way, the client needs to be reassured that

> ➘ *Common Pitfall*
> *Noisy Abreaction*
>
> Amanda abreacted during a desensitization session dealing with an unre-solved bereavement. Her cries built up into howls of grief and her thera-pist, Hayley, became very concerned that people in the adjacent office would hear. She stopped the desensitization.
>
> Both Amanda and Hayley were scared by the intensity of her abreaction and continued with a different therapeutic approach.
>
> With hindsight, Hayley felt that she could have continued the DAS but lacked the confidence in herself to do so. She also ensured that, with any further EMDR clients, her colleagues would be aware of the possibilities of noisy abreaction. She could then relax knowing that her session would not be interrupted by a concerned member of staff.

this is normal, that they are unlikely to complete the urge, and that they can stop at any point.

The real problem with abreaction is when clients feel that they can-not tolerate it. Preparing clients for heightened affect prior to desensiti-zation and reminding them of their ability to manage this should be done prior to utilizing DAS.

> *Case Example*
> *Abreaction*
>
> Brandon had a fear that he would vomit during desensitization. For him, reassurance that his therapist would not be horrified and reject him if this happened was enough.
>
> The therapist asked if there was anything else that would help. After a slight pause, Brandon asked if it would be okay to have a bin on his knee while he worked on the incident. His therapist readily agreed.

> ## ↘ *Common Pitfall*
> ## *Misunderstanding What Will Happen*
>
> As soon as Robert began a set of EM, his client Maureen relaxed her expression and posture. At the end of the set, Robert asked for feedback.
>
> "What do you get now?"
>
> "Nothing, just really relaxed," Maureen sighed.
>
> A little perplexed, Robert continued, "Okay just go with that."
>
> Maureen began to smile contentedly during subsequent sets. Despite returning to the original target, with its SUDS of 7/10, Maureen continued to have the same response. EM just seemed to relax her completely, and she was very happy with this.
>
> Robert needed to check out whether Maureen was struggling to keep a dual focus of attention or possibly was even telling him what she thought he wanted to hear to be a "good patient." Maureen revealed that she was simply letting the target slip away and following the lights to relax. Robert had to return to preparation, ensuring Maureen fully understood the nature of EMDR before proceeding.

With a good therapeutic relationship, simple reassurance will often suffice. Supportive comments such as

It's over

This is just old stuff buried

You survived the incident and now you are letting go of the emotions that were trapped with it

You are safe, I am here with you.

The abreaction will generally peak and then fall away, but if the client is still having difficulties tolerating the reaction, other strategies can be used so that continued processing is possible.

- Increasing the speed or length of sets of DAS can be compared with being in a dark train tunnel and hastening the journey

- Changing modality, for example, asking the client to focus on physical sensations rather than distressing images
- Changing to audio or tapping DAS as visual images are often the most emotionally arousing
- Slowing down DAS to control overwhelming processing
- Distancing techniques can be used such as watching the event unfold on a screen or reducing color and brightness of an image.

Clients should be empowered and feel able to stop should they need to do so without being judged. Common sense should be used. If an abreaction is too intense and the therapist's interventions are not having an impact, the therapist should stop DAS and reground the client in the here and now, before working collaboratively with the client on how to proceed.

Case Example
Distractions

Some clients get distracted and are unable to retain a dual focus of attention.

In his first desensitization session, after the initial set of EMs, John was asked what he noticed.

John: Nothing. I was just watching your fingers. I find it hard to think about the image and watch the movements as well. As soon as you started moving your hand, the image just went as I was concentrating on what you were doing.

Therapist: That's fine. Don't worry about this. Sometimes it takes a few moments for us to get into the processing. What I'd like you to do is start this again and, if the image disappears again, just notice what is happening to your negative thought, the body sensations, and/or emotions rather than just the image.

Further, DAS were utilized and John was able to retain his attention on his body sensations and emotions while following the EM.

An alternative strategy would have been to change the method of DAS. Some clients are less distracted by tapping or audio DAS. It is crucial to foster a sense of hope and experimentation to prevent feelings of failure.

> ### Case Example
> ### Feedback
>
> Abdul was asked for feedback following the first set of EM during desensitization of his experience of workplace bullying.
>
> **Therapist**: What do you notice now?
>
> **Abdul**: Nothing's changed. It's still the same.
>
> **Therapist**: Which bit is still the same?
>
> **Abdul**: The image, it's not changed.
>
> **Therapist**: If you just scan your emotions, do you notice any changes there?
>
> **Abdul**: No, they're still the same.
>
> **Therapist**: What about your physical sensations?
>
> **Abdul**: No change.
>
> **Therapist**: And your thoughts?
>
> **Abdul**: I keep thinking about when I was little and I felt like such a disappointment to my parents.
>
> **Therapist**: Just notice that . . .

The debrief is particularly important following a session during which the client abreacts. The therapist should incorporate space in the session for "the dust to settle" and for clients to make some sense of their experience and distance themselves from it. See chapter 6 for further information on closure of sessions.

BLOCKED PROCESSING

Sometimes, therapists feel as though they have done all their preparation and are raring to go. They complete the first set and ask their client "what do you get now?" The response is "nothing." There are many possible reasons for the client reporting this, and it's helpful to clarify what "nothing" means.

Case Example
Expectations

Lorraine and her therapist were working on a memory of a humiliation at school. Lorraine reported that she was "getting nothing" after her first set of EM.

Her therapist asked her for feedback on the image, cognition, emotions, and body sensations but Lorraine insisted they had all gone as soon as the EM started and she now had "nothing."

Therapist: What's in your head right now?

Lorraine (in a resigned voice): You must think I'm stupid. I can't even get this right.

(The therapist recognized that this had resonance with the target memory and decided to continue with this line of thought.)

Therapist: Okay, I just want you to think about that and follow my fingers.

Lorraine: What? Think about me not getting this right? Not being able to do EMDR?

Therapist: Yes, and just notice what happens.

The feeling of being stupid and its associated affect intensified, and Lorraine's processing moved to related images of her school days. From then on, Lorraine was much more ready to share her feedback even when she doubted its relevance.

The therapist should consider whether clients understand what feedback is needed. Are there subtle changes that they have discounted, for example, the image is less sharp or being seen from a different perspective? Are they focusing on one modality, for example, the image?

Other reasons for blocks may be that the client is expecting to feel or see something specific and because this is not happening he or she is "getting nothing." If a client is feeling numb this could be a layer of emotion to process. Alternatively, the client may be censoring or discarding

---

⊘ *Whatever You Do, Don't Do This ...*

Cameron had experienced a particularly violent car-jacking. He had been sent to his company therapist who had recently trained in EMDR and she felt it would be "ideal" to help the client. The therapist was quite anxious that she only had eight sessions with the client and carried out the early phases quite quickly with the client. However, each time Cameron raised issues that the therapist did not deem as "relevant" to the memory being targeted, she told him to "just forget about that for now" and carried on to the desensitization phase. Ultimately, the client went back to his company and requested another therapist. The EMDR therapist explored the case in depth at supervision and identified that, in her enthusiasm to use EMDR, she had reinforced his negative cognition of "I am powerless" by setting her own agenda and not being client led.

---

material because it does not seem relevant. Having the wrong NC or PC may also create a block and may need to be reconsidered.

Insufficient preparation may also be causing problems. Clients may not have fully bought into the process. This may be because they do not really understand what they have to do and try to force the process. Maybe they have performance anxiety or unaddressed fears. They may not trust the therapeutic relationship or may be picking up on the therapist's anxiety. The therapist may notice that clients are trying to control their breathing or are pushing away emotions that are bubbling up. They may use words to intellectualize the process or provide a nonstop narrative that acts as a barrier to the underlying emotions. Sometimes they are not engaging with the therapy due to secondary gain or control issues.

Blocks, or looping, may occur at the start of DAS or during later sets. You may become aware of a block when you feel that clients are giving feedback that reflects no change in any modality. They seem stuck. As illustrated earlier, strategies for managing these blocks should initially be a minimal intervention. Therapists can change modality (as shown in the above examples), change the direction of EM, or change the speed, or even method, of DAS.

> ### ⇘ *Common Pitfall*
> ### *Secondary Gain*
>
> Luke was a senior fire-fighter who had been involved in a factory blaze when one of his close colleagues had been killed. It had been his decision to enter the building, and Luke had to face an investigation into his actions. Although he was cleared of any blame, he felt he was responsible. He met his colleague's wife at the funeral and described her as "broken." On desensitization, the SUDS reduced from 9 but remained high at 6 despite mechanical changes and a cognitive interweave. The therapist stopped DAS and explored with Luke what might be blocking their further reduction.
>
> She discovered that Luke felt that if he "removed the memory" of what had happened he would "forget his colleague" and his wife would still have to live with his death. After supervision, the therapist worked on the image of living without the intrusive images and the negative cognition that went with that. This was processed successfully and allowed Luke to continue desensitizing the incident.

COGNITIVE INTERWEAVES

The aim of the cognitive interweave is to help the client to make the connections he or she is not making spontaneously. The therapist offers statements that will help the client access positive information and connect it to the traumatic material. The golden rule is "minimal intervention first" and the mechanical strategies should precede a cognitive interweave. A short set of DAS should be used after the cognitive interweave to check its effect before continuing. Interweaves should be offered between sets rather than during sets when the client is immersed in the process.

The different types of cognitive interweave are elaborated in Shapiro (2001) and can include

- Providing new information
- Stimulating held information
- The adult perspective
- I am confused
- What if it were your child?
- Metaphors and analogies

- Let us pretend
- The Socratic method.

Where the target for processing is a representative event from a cluster of memories, for example, the worst or earliest memory of childhood

---

Case Example
Cognitive Interweave

Luke was a paramedic who had been involved in a serious train crash. Although injured and shaken himself, he had tended to the wounded passengers as best as he could. He was stuck with the image of an old man who was trapped in the wreckage and appealing for help. Luke had passed him by and helped others in the area. He could not understand why he had not helped the man and felt intense guilt and shame as he knew that the man had died at the scene.

Luke: I should have helped him.

(Despite mechanical changes, his feedback remained the same after several more sets indicating that his processing was blocked. His therapist offered the following cognitive interweave.)

Therapist: From what you told me about his injuries, do you think he could have been saved?

Luke: There's no way he could have survived those injuries. Even if I'd had all the equipment, I couldn't have saved him. I suppose I just wish I had been able to comfort him.

Therapist: What were you doing instead of comforting him?

Luke: I was stopping other people from dying—those I knew I could save.

Therapist: I want you to just think about that (applies DAS).

The therapist was stimulating information that Luke already held. He knew he had saved the lives of at least two others at the scene and the cognitive interweave allowed him to integrate this information and continue processing.

Chapter Resource 5.1 offers some suggestions for working with disproportionate or misplaced guilt.

Common Pitfall
The Therapist is Frightened to Intervene

William was a competent counselor but very conscious of his novice status as an EMDR therapist, and he was trying hard to focus on the protocol. During desensitization of a childhood abandonment, his client Faith gave the following feedback between sets.

Faith: I want to say how I'm feeling.

William: Just notice that.

Faith: I want someone to ask how I'm feeling.

William: Just notice that.

Faith: I want someone to ask me what I want to do.

William: Just notice that.

William could possibly have intervened earlier as a pattern of stuckness was emerging.

A simple intervention, rather than "just notice that" could have been to say,

"Tell me how you are feeling?"

"How are you feeling?"

"What do you want to do?"

However, because William was unsure whether he was "allowed" to offer this intervention, he didn't follow his instinctual response. In supervision, he said

"It felt as though Faith was stuck, but I didn't know if this was a cognitive interweave as I couldn't decide what type it was."

abuse, there would usually be a generalization effect with the other similar events. Where this generalization fails to occur naturally, cognitive interweaves can be used to help make connections.

As you become more confident with the standard protocol, you will feel more comfortable using more imaginative interweaves at different stages. However, initially it is advisable to develop your skills step by step.

CASE STUDY: EMMA'S DESENSITIZATION SESSION

Target memory	Emma being shouted at by her mother
Image	Mother crying and shouting
Negative cognition	It is my fault
Positive cognition and VOC	It is not my fault
	VOC = 2
Emotions	Fear, shame, guilt, sadness
SUDS	8/10
Location of body sensations	Nausea, feels heat rising up neck, flushed

Notes: During desensitization, Emma's emotions raised, and tears streamed from her eyes. She was able to continue with EMs and I quietly reassured her, "You're doing really well."

During subsequent sets, her feedback was as follows: "I remember what we did now—we'd spilled a carton of orange juice on the carpet."

"Mum was really upset."

"I feel angry—I'm wondering where my dad is? Why isn't he here to help us and make her feel better?"

"My stomach's churning."

Another memory arose that she had not mentioned in the assessment.

"I'm thinking about Sammy, my rabbit."

Emma became more tearful at this point and we moved to tapping.

"He's dead, and it's my fault."

"My mum and dad are cross with me, telling me not to cry as I should have looked after him better."

"I loved him."

"I forgot to feed him one day. I'd been excited about getting ready for a birthday party and had left him. He must have starved to death."

"It was my fault. I was really cruel putting myself first, wanting to look nice for the party and forgetting Sammy."

Emma continued to cry but was able to resume EM. After another couple of sets, she was still unwavering about her responsibility in the matter. I tried changing EM direction, then modality, with no effect, so offered a cognitive interweave:

"Apart from the day of the party, did you care for Sammy properly? (Emma nods emphatically.) I'm confused. You're telling me then that he starved to death in one day? Does that sound right to you?"

Emma stopped and looked at me puzzled. I could almost see the link being made.

"No, he couldn't have."

I directed her to just think about that and continued the EM.

"That would be impossible."

"It must have been something else."

"He was pretty old for a rabbit."

Emma moved quickly through from that point. (I could have offered an alternative interweave by asking her to consider one of her nieces in that position. That may have had the same results but I went with what felt right at the time.) Emma continued with EM and reported a more compassionate self-evaluation.

"I loved that rabbit."

"I always wanted another pet, but was scared that I would somehow harm it."

"I'd really like to get myself a little cat. Maybe now I could do that."

The session ended on this note because we were running short of time. If we had had longer, I would have returned to the original target of her mother shouting at her.

However, we ended with her safe place exercise and Emma spontaneously reported that a small, grey kitten had joined her sitting on the jetty and watching the sunset.

Emma left with instructions on self-care, keeping her journal, and how to contact me in the interim should any disturbance arise that she was troubled by.

FREQUENTLY ASKED QUESTIONS

Q: **My client is describing intrusive images of how his friend died. Even though he didn't witness it he is imagining how it was. Can I target this fantasy image or choose something he did see?**

A: Whatever the client presents is his or her representation of the incident, even if it is imaginary or metaphorical, therefore it should be processed in the normal way.

Q: **I had a client who asked me to "just get on with it" when we started the desensitization. I felt under a lot of pressure and the session was unproductive. In the earlier phases, she has engaged well and completed set tasks. However, with the**

desensitization I feel I am being given all the responsibility and control. What should I do?

A: You should always ensure that the client is fully engaged in the process as this is a key element of EMDR. Being passive is not an option, therefore it is important to explore the client's reticence in detail and explain the importance of being proactive. She may have unaddressed fears or be used to taking a passive role in her life when dealing with difficult issues. Even during desensitization, a collaborative approach is required for optimal results.

Q: **In a desensitization session recently, my client had a lengthy and ongoing reaction. She told me she was okay to continue and was well aware of her stop sign. I was aware of the diminishing time and my own fatigue but didn't feel able to interrupt her when she was at a peak of emotion. This "peak" showed no signs of abating. I'm dreading this happening again and need to know how I handle it.**

A: This can be a sensitive issue to address and raises the issues of boundaries, client preparation, session time management, and ensuring a degree of flexibility. Indicators for stopping desensitization as an incomplete session, may include insufficient time, client fatigue, or reaching a relatively calm place. We would normally encourage the completion of a peak and its subsequent drop in affect. However, in your example, the peak doesn't appear to be reducing, and your client wishes to continue. Have you considered whether she is looping? If so, changing the mechanics and then offering a cognitive interweave may be appropriate. If she is not looping, you may need to take control and ask her to stop, do a short debrief, explain approximately how much processing time is left, and ask her how she would like to proceed, thus giving her choice and control.

Q: **When I get to Phase 4, how often should I be doing desensitization sessions?**

A: This will depend on many factors including the client's resilience, outside stressors intruding on the work, and the depth of work being done. You should use your clinical judgment after considering them. Desensitization can be hard work so it can be tough to do a desensitization session every week. It may be better to allow sessions for consolidating learning and taking a respite from very heavy work. However, too many breaks can delay recovery and lose momentum or signify an underlying avoidance (by therapist or client) to confront traumatic material. It is good practice to use some sessions for review of progress and consolidation, but it can be frustrating if these are overly used.

LEARNING SUMMARY

You should feel confident that you are able to:

- Explain desensitization fully and clearly to your client
- Work through all the channels of association related to the target memory
- Be clear of your role during desensitization
- Help your client to manage abreactions during the EMDR desensitization
- Have a range of strategies for when processing is blocked, always using minimal interventions first.

RESOURCES

5.1: Working With Guilt

When clients become blocked with an issue around guilt, it can sometimes be difficult to think of appropriate Cognitive Interweaves. Here are some suggestions:

- Work to distribute responsibility, using all possible contributors, use a percentage method.
- Use an outside perspective (e.g., if that was your child).

Useful Questions to Ask

How did you know what was going to happen?

How much time did you have to make up your mind about what to do?

What did you do that you think was okay?

If it had been someone else rather than you who was present, what do you think that person would have done?

What would you have said/done if someone else had done the same thing under the same circumstances?

How easy was it to influence what happened?

What was the reason you did what you did?

What you did at the time made sense to you then, otherwise you wouldn't have done it! Ask yourself, "why did it make sense to me then?"

6   Moving Out of Dark Places

Chapter 6 considers Phases 5–8, installation, body scan, closure, and reevaluation. EMDR is not always a linear process. Therapists may find themselves returning to earlier phases and need to be flexible in their adherence to the protocol. This chapter will look at managing incomplete sessions—you will have these. As with all therapy, what happens between the sessions is just as important as what happens in the sessions. Because clients will continue processing after you have stopped DAS, they should be prepared for ongoing disturbance and be able to capture surfacing material. Therapists will need to reevaluate their treatment plan and possibly work with what has come up between sessions.

INSTALLATION

As stated in chapter 4, EMDR does not just desensitize a memory but links it to more adaptive knowledge. The installation phase is concerned with integrating the positive cognition (PC) with the targeted memory. Sometimes, during desensitization, clients begin to make spontaneous statements of their PC such as "I am a good person." This can be reinforced with further DAS, but the therapist should always return to the original target and specifically link the PC with that.

The PC may have changed from the initial one chosen and it is common for it to have developed from a fairly neutral one, for example, "It's over" to a more empowered one, "It's made me a safer driver." The PC should be checked for ecological validity and rated on the VOC scale.

CASE STUDY: EMMA'S INSTALLATION

At her next session, Emma and her therapist had continued to work on the memory of her mother being upset and shouting at her.

Her NC had been, "It's my fault" and, in this session, her SUDS had reduced to 0 from an initial 5. The previous session had reduced much of the intensity.

Therapist: So do the words "It's not my fault" fit? Or is there something else that would fit better?

Emma: No, those words sound fine. I now know that it wasn't my fault. She was struggling with the breakdown of her marriage, and our little accident with the orange juice must have just been the last straw. She was at breaking point and letting off steam.

Therapist: And if you think about the words "It's not my fault" and that image, how true do they feel right now, on the scale of 1 to 7?

Emma: 7 is completely true? It's a 7.

Therapist: Okay, just think about that (short sets of DAS).

Emma: That feels really peaceful. I just want to go home now and give my mother a hug.

The PC should be checked using the VOC to address any blocks during the installation phase. Clients sometimes have "gremlins" lurking. The therapist should be alert to an unsaid "but. . ." and give the client permission to raise these doubts by explaining that they are not a sign that the session has "failed." These residual issues may be a new NC that needs then to be processed or a PC that is not ecologically valid as a completely true statement. You may need to check for blocking beliefs.

BODY SCAN

Phase 6 is the body scan where the client should be asked to hold the original memory, while considering the PC, and check his or her body for any tension or sensation. The therapist should then target this with DAS.

> ### ➘ *Common Pitfall*
> ### *VOC Doesn't Reach 6 or 7*
>
> Sally had worked on her memory of domestic violence. Although she was out of the relationship, she could not bring her PC of "I'm safe now" to feel completely true. On exploring this, she realized it was due to the imminent release from prison of her violent ex-partner. This event then became a focus for further therapeutic (and practical) work.

CASE STUDY: EMMA'S BODY SCAN

Therapist: Sometimes, our memories are stored in our body as physical sensations and it's important to check for and then release these parts. When you think about your mother shouting at you and the thought "It's not my fault," I'd like you just to mentally scan your entire body. Check out from your head to your toes to see if there is any discomfort or tension—anything that your body is telling you.

Emma closes her eyes and mentally scans as requested.

Emma: I've got a little tightness in my chest. Not a great deal, just a little.

Therapist: Okay, we'll do some more eye movements on this. Just like with the other EM, you may find that the sensations change, increase or decrease, or that different material comes up. Don't worry about this. We'll just go with the flow as before.

(DAS applied.)

Therapist: What do you notice now?

Emma: The tightness has increased and I'm getting butterflies in my stomach.

Therapist: Okay, just notice that.

Further sets of EM lead to a decrease in the physical sensations until Emma reported feeling calm and peaceful.

It is important to be specific when asking for body sensations. For example, a client who reports a headache that does not change with further DAS, "I've still got a headache," may actually be noticing changes in the severity, location, or type of sensation. Asking for clear feedback will allow you to determine whether this is the case.

> ### *Case Example*
> ### *Body Scan*
>
> Sometimes it can feel as though the physical sensations are being chased around the client's body. On his body scan, Mason reported a feeling of butterflies in his stomach. His therapist asked him just to be aware of this while she utilized DAS. He then reported additional tension in his legs, arms, and shoulders. During further sets, this tension increased then fell away only to be replaced by an ache at the front of his head and a clench-ing in his jaw. More DAS lead to a tingling in his hands and feet. Again, he was just asked to notice this. Further sets lead to reports of lowering tension and ultimately a feeling of calm in his solar plexus.

For some clients, the body scan and resulting DAS can lead to other material surfacing. This may be memories, thoughts, and images relating to the original target or another memory in the network. You will need to consider whether you can target this material now, return to the assess-ment phase, or deal with these in a separate session and treat this as an incomplete session. Positive body sensations can be enhanced with DAS if it feels appropriate.

CLOSURE

Closure is important at the end of any therapy, and particularly so after EMDR desensitization. Not closing a session properly is a bit like a man-ager offering a member of staff a lift home from work after a very stressful day, and then dropping him or her off in the middle of nowhere without a map. He or she will be disorientated, even more stressed, and have no clues about what to do next or what is going to happen. This is the part of the session when the client is brought out of negative affect into balanced or positive affect. The client is then engaged cognitively and encouraged to think about the next steps. The aim is to leave the client in as positive a state of mind as possible, ensuring that he or she is capable of getting home safely. As such, it is important to allow sufficient time for closure, debriefing, safety assessment, and homework. After the first session of DAS, some therapists will consider sessions as having three parts. The first part consists of reviewing the client's progress since the last session and defining the target for desensitization at this session (reevaluation), which is discussed later. The second part is targeting the memory with DAS, and the third part is for closure.

One of the recommendations made during EMDR training courses is that the therapist offers the client contact between sessions, particularly in the early stages. Although this is individual to the therapist, it is important that boundaries are still applied to this contact. This may seem obvious, but novice EMDR therapists can be anxious about how clients will react following desensitization. Because of the power and sometimes the speed of EMDR, therapists are keen to ensure that their clients are okay and may make statements such as "if you are struggling between sessions, give me a ring." This can give the message that the therapist is not expecting the client to cope, in addition to extending an open-ended invitation to ring you at 3 a.m.! Therapists should be aware of choosing their words carefully. Again, it is about getting the balance right! In addition, it may be helpful to be aware of the spacing of sessions because vulnerable clients may need additional sessions initially as they become accustomed to processing difficult material.

Complete sessions occur when you reach the end of all channels of association and the SUDS equal zero. However, do not always expect

---

⟩ *Common Pitfall*
Running Out of Time

It can be tempting to keep going with DAS when you feel there is an imminent breakthrough. Lois had already experienced several EMDR desensitization sessions and was becoming accustomed to her response to EMDR. She was processing a new childhood memory and wanted to "just get this bit done," even though the session was coming to a close. Encouraged by her client's progress, the therapist decided to continue with DAS. Unfortunately, Lois connected to another channel of association and started to abreact. The session had to be extended to work with the abreaction and then included a shorter debrief and closure. This resulted in the therapist having no time to rest between clients and feeling exhausted at the end of the day. At the following session, Lois reported that she had experienced higher levels of anxiety than usual between sessions.

this. Once the DAS has been stopped, clients need to be debriefed and a check made on how they are feeling. Useful questions can be

What has been the most important thing for you about today's session?

Have you gained any insights into what's happening for you?

Was there anything that surprised you in that session?

Some therapists make notes during desensitization. This can be helpful, but clients should be forewarned of this and the reasons for it to prevent them becoming self-conscious in their feedback. The client may like feedback on the main themes that came up. However, analysis should be avoided.

The therapist should ensure that the clients have regained emotional balance before they leave the consulting room. A range of methods can be used to achieve this, for example, a relaxation technique such as the light stream exercise or safe place (Shapiro, 2001). Clients should be reminded of how to self-soothe. If clients have been working on early childhood memories, they can be encouraged to think about what would make their inner child feel nurtured. Therapists can draw on their existing range of skills in this area and can ask themselves the question "what would I suggest if I wasn't using EMDR?"

Clients can be brought back into the cognitive domain with questions such as

What are your plans for the rest of the day (the next few days)?

What are you going to do to look after yourself?

Can you foresee any problems over the next week that you will need to deal with? (Suggest that, if possible, they avoid stressful situations and people. This serves as a reminder to clients that they are working hard and deserve some "me" time.)

What do you need to get by over the next week?

Do you have any worries about how you will be?

Remind your clients before they leave that they will carry on processing material, which may or may not be in their awareness, for some time after they have left the consulting room. Chapter Resource 6.1 shows an

---

⊘ *Whatever You Do, Don't Do This . . .*

Mary had recently completed her Level 1 EMDR, and her current long-term client had agreed to work on a particular issue using EMDR. Mary carried out the early phases of EMDR and then carried out the desensitization session. In her enthusiasm to help the client, she left insufficient time at the end of the session to stabilize the client and the session ended quite abruptly. On the way home, her client was involved in a minor road traffic collision.

---

example handout on the kinds of experience that individuals may have. This can normalize any between-session disturbance, and it increases the client's sense of control and understanding should reactions arise.

As stated in chapter 5, EMDR therapists can expect to have incomplete sessions, and preparing the client for the possibility of this happening prevents or reduces disappointment and clients' statements such as "that didn't work" or "what was that all about?" Maintaining a sense of hope fuels the clients' engagement in the ongoing process. By explaining that they have worked on part of the memory, the therapist can ensure that clients feel they have accomplished something.

Incomplete sessions will mean that there are residual symptoms left from an incident. As a result, at the extreme end of the spectrum, the client could initially be emotional, and consequently, have difficulty accessing his or her problem-solving skills. However, other individuals may, for example, get angry but need to stay angry for a while, and this can be processed on their next attendance if necessary. It is important to bear in mind client safety between sessions, including managing risk, such as suicide, self-harm, addictions, and violent outbursts. The therapist's assessment of risk should be reviewed in each session.

At the beginning of each new session, the therapist will assess the progress being made, will look for surfacing material and challenges that may have arisen, and will study how these changes will have an impact on the overall treatment plan. Consequently, this provides the rationale for keeping a journal or log in between sessions to ensure a spirit of collaborative detective work. Chapter Resource 6.2 offers a suggested format for the journal. The client has a big responsibility to bring feedback

---

Case Example
Client Disappointment

Mandy had been suffering from PTSD for several years following a boating accident where she nearly drowned, and her father was killed. After hearing of a friend who had successfully dealt with a recent trauma using EMDR psychotherapy, she decided to try it herself. She had high expectations.

After her first desensitization session, her SUDS had reduced from 9 to 5; she was quite disappointed and felt that it was not working. Her therapist Jimmy asked her how long she had suffered from PTSD, Mandy replied that it had been about 23 years. Jimmy then asked her how long the desensitization part of that session had lasted. Looking slightly bemused, she replied "about 40 minutes," Jimmy went on, "so you have had PTSD for 23 years, and in 40 minutes, your level of disturbance has moved from 9 to 5. What does that tell you?"

Mandy realized she had, in fact, begun to process the incident.

---

and should be well prepared for this in the closure phase. Clients will, however, differ in their compliance with this request. There is a continuum from the clients who report "nothing much happened" to clients who bring journals that they wish to pore over.

➘ *Common Pitfall*
Client Feedback

Natalie never remembered to keep a journal, despite being provided with a sample log. She always reported that nothing had happened and seemed to feel that, provided she turned up on time each time, this was her only responsibility.

Carlos was at the opposite end of the spectrum and kept meticulous notes detailing changes, dreams, and insights. While much useful information was within the notes, the therapist found that the bulk of the session was being spent on this feedback.

Case Example
Rapid Results

Charlotte had been in an armed raid. She was particularly troubled by the image of a hooded robber holding a machete. This part of the memory was targeted along with her negative cognition of "I'm in danger," feelings of panic, and sensations of a tight chest and knotted stomach (SUDS 9).

During desensitization, Charlotte reported feeling temporarily more agitated and then, with subsequent sets, calmer. She stated the memory became "like a picture on the table that I can just blow away" and proceeded to do just that. The complete memory was targeted in just six sets with a spontaneous PC of "it's over, they're gone."

Both Charlotte and her therapist were delighted with such a quick result, although there was also a sense of "this was too good, it would not last." On reevaluation at the next session, the SUDS were still at 0 and termination of therapy seemed appropriate. To guard against her feeling that this was a temporary change, they agreed to a further session to ensure no other material had surfaced. At that session, a "safety net" appointment was made for 3 months' time with the flexibility to bring this forward if needed or cancel closer to the time if not needed.

Charlotte rang a few days before the appointment to say she was doing well and had had no further issues related to the armed raid.

Sometimes EMDR works spectacularly well and there can be a sense of disbelief that this is a permanent and conclusive change.

REEVALUATION

Issues that need to be considered on reevaluation include the following.

Symptoms

How successfully have clients managed ongoing disturbance? Do they need to strengthen coping strategies? Are they actually using the coping strategies when required? Successful use can be encouraged and

---

⊘ *Whatever You Do, Don't Do This...*

Desensitization should never be used on a final session because it is not possible to predict what could surface.

Alan found this out the hard way. He had seen his therapist about an armed raid in the bank where he worked. The desensitization session had gone really well, his SUDS reduced to 0 and a VOC of 7 for his PC of "It's over." Along with his therapist, he made an agreement that he did not really need to come back. "EMDR had been a success."

However, over the following days and weeks, Alan's anxiety returned along with memories of being threatened by his abusive stepfather when he was young. Alan ignored the subtle change at first and thought his other memories would go away, but his symptoms became quite debilitating. Alan did not feel able to return to the therapist because he felt he was a failure, EMDR had not worked, and he would always feel like this. It was not until after an unsuccessful suicide attempt that he would again access therapy.

---

reinforced, but the therapist should be alert to the need to change or add to strategies. Reevaluation should reveal whether the client has fully understood the need for them or has no faith in their ability to help. Clients may report symptoms reducing or new ones arising. These can be a source of new information. For example, with a client who reveals he or she has felt depressed following desensitization, the therapist may wish to explore what is the NC behind this new emotion. Dreams can also provide useful information and may be usefully targeted.

Changes

Evidence of readjustment should be identified. Clients often report such evidence, but have not recognized it as progress or have dismissed it.

Problems with clients' engagement in the process may surface at any point during therapy such as canceling or "forgetting" sessions or not keeping their journal or doing their homework. These may indicate unexpressed fears, ambivalence about the therapy, or lack of faith in the process.

> **Case Example**
> **Incomplete History**
>
> Lauren had been abducted by an ex-boyfriend when she had tried to end the relationship. He had held her captive for a week. Her family was unaware of her situation because her boyfriend had been emotionally abusive and controlling and had stopped her contacting her family on a regular basis. However, she had managed to escape and contact the police and her sister. As this was a major trauma, the therapist worked on face validity and skated over her childhood history. A desensitization session targeted the abduction and, although incomplete, the SUDS fell from 9/10 to 4/10.
>
> On reevaluation, however, Lauren reported they were back at a 9. The therapist decided to use the "floatback" technique, and Lauren told her that when she was a young child, she had been locked in the cupboard under the stairs by her father for watching TV instead of doing her homework. This feeder memory was processed, and the therapist was able to continue with desensitization on the abduction.

In complex cases particularly, a regular overview of the therapy returning to the initial presenting problems and goals will maintain a focus and sense of progress.

Surfacing Material

The importance of taking a thorough history can become apparent at this stage, as feeder memories may surface. Their existence may be suspected when progress from an earlier session is not maintained.

Sometimes, no matter how thorough the history taking has been, clients are not aware of a feeder memory until after the original target has been started. They may have discounted it as important or blocked it from their awareness.

TREATMENT PLAN

All of the above information needs to be considered in respect of the overall treatment plan. As a reminder, the treatment plan identified

Case Example
New Information Arises

Kieran was asked to keep a journal between sessions but kept "forgetting." Although the sessions were going well, it was not until the fourth desensitization session that he remembered that every time he smelled newly mown grass, he would have intrusive memories and bad dreams of the severe bullying he had experienced at school. Once this had been identified, the therapist helped him to access the connecting memory and the trigger was desensitized. Had Kieran kept the journal, this may have been identified much earlier and dealt with.

specific targets for reprocessing. These included the past memories that appeared to have set the pathology in process, the present situations that exacerbate this dysfunction, and the desired future response.

First, the therapist needs to consider whether the previous session's target has been resolved, by checking the SUDS and VOC. The target memory may need further processing with DAS. However, if the target carries no level of disturbance and the PC has been successfully installed, then the therapist can move on to other memories. These other targets may be part of the initial list including the touchstone memory and other past memories or may be material that has been activated or surfaced during the course of therapy.

Although clients may report that their reactions in respect of a memory are calmer and less anxious, the SUDS cannot in every case be expected to go to a zero. Therapists should be alert to ecological validity and their client's value system and the occasions when, for the client, "it wouldn't be right" for an incident to carry a zero rating, for example, where someone had died. Similarly, EMDR is not going to process appropriate fears, that is, when the threat is still current.

If no further memories need addressing from the past, then the therapist should move onto considering present situations that trigger the dysfunction. Often, when the past has been cleared, there is a knock-on effect for current issues. For example, a client whose present day anxiety was rooted in childhood experiences may feel more confident generally once those experiences are healed. A review of the therapeutic goals is

Case Example
Future Template

Isaac came to EMDR therapy for his severe dental phobia.

History taking revealed this to be as a result of an accident in childhood where he had lost his front teeth. Luckily these were his "baby teeth," but Isaac remembered being pinned down in the hospital while the fragments were removed from his bleeding mouth. DAS was used to target this memory and two other related ones from his past where he had had a similar lack of control.

He found that the present triggers disappeared, and, finally, his therapist asked him to imagine a visit to the dentist. Using DAS they desensitized:

Making an appointment

The journey to the dentist

Signing in at reception

Sitting in the waiting room

Hearing the drill

Sitting in the dentist chair

Having treatment

Going home

Isaac was able to imagine all this as a video without any disturbance. The therapist helped him plan experiments that could be used to test out his phobia. Any disturbances were targeted along the way, and Isaac, ultimately, lost his fear and was able to have long overdue treatment without distress.

useful here. As the client changes, he or she and the people around them need to adjust appropriately. Help may be needed in doing so.

Finally, clients may have apprehensions about the future that may be addressed with DAS. Clients who have experienced complex or childhood trauma may be lacking in early developmental experiences. Modeling, education on social skills, and testing out new behaviors will now be the focus of therapy. Moving the client toward an empowered

> ⇘ *Common Pitfall*
> ## *Life Gets in the Way of Therapy*
>
> As with any therapy, clients will sometimes find that something occurs that disrupts the therapeutic plan. This may be an unexpected crisis, such as a relationship breakdown or being diagnosed with cancer, and clients will need support in making adjustments in their present life.
>
> However, sometimes these will be less major events, such as escalating intrafamilial tensions or problems in the workplace. Jack reported that his client Cynthia was having problems with a workmate. An impending business event was preying on her mind, and she spent two sessions in tears discussing how manipulative and cruel her colleague was being. Jack began working at cognitively challenging her realistic and unrealistic thoughts around the situation. He felt that this was distracting from the therapy and that he was "fire-fighting," but not making any progress with her treatment plan. During consultation, he realized that the present day situation was based on her negative cognition of being helpless in a dysfunctional family—the underlying theme to the previous EMDR they had been working on. He expressed this to Cynthia, and they successfully returned to their work on the root of the problem.

and independent future is the goal, although clients also need to know that it is not a failure to return to therapy if help is needed with new challenges.

CASE STUDY: EMMA'S REEVALUATION

Emma returned following her session (as shown in chapter 5). She had been keeping her journal and noticing changes in her thoughts, behaviors, and feelings.

"I was quite buoyant after the session and I've been much more relaxed with my mother. However, I noticed after a couple of days that I was thinking much more about what happened, you know recently, and feeling panicky. I had a horrible dream last night where I was being chased by a man. I was running down a road and knocking on doors for help but people either didn't answer or told me to go away and stop bothering them. Nobody else seemed able to see him."

She also reported she was feeling angry. It appeared that, as her sense of responsibility was lifted, she had connected with the sense of fear.

When I checked the previous week's target and its associated SUDS, these were still 0 as were those relating to the death of her pet rabbit. I gave her the following analogy.

"Sometimes it's as if you hold a hand up right in front of your face and all you can see is that hand. When you take it away, you realize what is behind it and then you can deal with that. When you first started, you were very focused on your sense of responsibility and now that that has lessened, the other emotions and thoughts can be seen."

We agreed that the next target would be the childhood molestation and the anxiety she felt around it. Emma was less troubled by her aunt's reaction now.

"I can see that she was shocked and didn't know what to do. She probably had issues of her own around responsibility. After all, I was in her care."

Therapy continued with the reprocessing of this and other memories, including, finally, the rape itself.

FINAL OUTCOME FOR EMMA

Once her past memories could be accessed without disturbance, we worked with her anxieties about dressing up and going away. Together we set some simple tasks, initially getting dressed up for a meal with a couple of trusted friends. Emma's confidence built quickly although further DAS was used around her successful rehabilitation back to work.

Toward the end of therapy, Emma decided to go to the police and report the rape. This is always a difficult issue in such cases and can be hard for the therapist to maintain impartiality. Indeed some therapeutic settings will impose directions to act particularly where childhood abuse was revealed. It is crucial that the therapist is clear on their ethical and legal requirements and takes advice where necessary on the limits of confidentiality. Emma wrestled with her feelings on what to do. She worried about Duncan attacking someone else and about the effect on herself of going through the court process. Realistically, her chances of a successful prosecution were low. In the end, she decided that she did not expect a result but wanted to feel she'd done what she could to protect other women.

At the end of therapy, Emma was confident and assertive and reported a much improved relationship with her mother. She was also less driven at work yet seemed to be getting the same results according to a recent appraisal.

"I've started to realize that I don't have to make people like me so long as I like myself. It's okay to make mistakes—it doesn't mean the world ends. Life is for living as well as for working. I never believed that something so strange could actually make such deep changes. When my therapist described EMDR, I was a little skeptical but desperate to change how I was feeling. I have to admit I was a little reluctant at first to work on the early memories, but my therapist explained the rationale and it made sense. I wouldn't have believed that it would make such deep changes. I've moved back into my own home ... and I've got myself a little cat!"

FREQUENTLY ASKED QUESTIONS

Q: **On reevaluation, my client still rated her serious accident as having SUDs of 8/10 but reported zero emotion and body sensation associated with it. What should I do?**

A: First, you should clarify what it is that the client is measuring. Is she separating the present from the past, for example, it WAS a bad thing and so will always be an 8/10, rather than this is how it feels now. If there is still a current level of disturbance then that should be targeted.

Q: **On the body scan, my client reported that she has a body sensation but it is one with which she came to the session. Do I persist with processing this?**

A: It is useful to keep an open mind on this issue. If time permits, you could target the body sensation as there is a potential that it is somatically linked to the traumatic event(s). For example, a client had experienced severe menstrual pain that her physician couldn't explain following a miscarriage. This had worsened as she had entered therapy and was dealing with her grief but she had not linked the two. However, you should also be aware that it may be unrelated. The client can be encouraged to notice body sensations throughout the week and record this in her journal for reevaluation at her next session.

Q: **I had a very intense session with a client and, although an incomplete session, stopped DAS at a calm place. During the debrief my client became very upset, and I didn't know whether to resume desensitization or just take the client to a**

safe place? I decided to restart the DAS with my client "just thinking about the current emotion," and we cleared the material quite quickly but I'm not sure I did the right thing.

A: There are factors to consider when making your clinical judgment on this. Clients need to be emotionally stabilized when they leave you. Time will be a factor and it is always wise to factor in additional time as a buffer when doing desensitization work. It may be that you ask clients what they need and base your response on this.

Q: **My client won't keep a journal.**

A: Have they understood the importance of this? Are they engaged with the process? What is stopping them, for example, lack of family support, privacy? Gently remind them of their responsibilities and that they are depriving both of you of helpful material. Changes should be recorded, no matter how seemingly irrelevant—that may be the missing piece in the jigsaw. Many people find that when they review their log, before or at the beginning of their next session, they have recorded significant things in between sessions that they had already forgotten about.

LEARNING SUMMARY

You should feel confident that you are able to:

- Install the PC
- Carry out a body scan
- Close a session effectively whether complete or incomplete
- Encourage the client to self-monitor between sessions
- Reevaluate progress at the start of each session and at other appropriate points.

Use the three-pronged approach to target the past, present, and future successfully.

RESOURCES

6.1: Information Sheet for Clients: What You MAY Experience After an EMDR Session

Following EMDR, processing will continue as your brain assimilates and integrates all the information. This is a positive sign that material is being processed. Below are examples of what other clients have described between sessions. You may want to add your own!

You may feel tired for the rest of the day

You may feel energized

Some people experience physical reactions (e.g., a headache)

Some people report a "cotton wool" feeling in their head

You may feel as if "a weight has been lifted"

You may get a sense that something has changed, but you are not sure what

You may experience short-term lack of concentration—"brain feels like it has gone into slow motion"

You may experience "echoes" of the memory you have been working on, in other words, you may get a faint reminder of parts of the incident between sessions

You may be more emotional

Other related or apparently unrelated memories may surface

As processing continues after the session, you may experience insights

You may have more vivid dreams.

Although this list is by no means exhaustive, the reactions are all a perfectly normal part of EMDR. However, if you are concerned by anything in between our sessions, please do not hesitate to contact me. It is recommended that you keep a journal to record your individual experience and bring it back for discussion at our next appointment.

Telephone No:	
For telephone contact, my hours of availability are:	
Alternative sources of support (include client's own resources):	

6.2: Example Log

Things I have noticed this week (dates)

DAY	THOUGHTS	FEELINGS	BODY SENSATIONS	BEHAVIORS	INTERACTIONS WITH OTHERS	DREAMS	OTHER MEMORIES	INSIGHTS
Monday								
Tuesday								
Wednesday								
Thursday								
Friday								
Saturday								
Sunday								

7 You Matter Too!

This final chapter focuses on the important topic of practitioners' self-care. Traumatic events adversely affect many people during their lifetime, and the primary focus of support services is on helping the individual, group, or community to recover from this experience. However, helping professionals, and particularly EMDR practitioners, who come into contact with traumatized individuals, are at risk of absorbing their distress. This can result in psychological injury to the helpers. Awareness and acknowledgment of these risks is the first step in addressing them, yet there is considerable stigma in admitting to secondary trauma. The question of who cares for the caregiver is often an afterthought in training and organizational settings.

This chapter provides an overview of psychological injury including the constructs of compassion fatigue (CF), vicarious trauma (VT), and burnout. The causal factors involved in developing these injuries are examined with an emphasis on the raised risks for EMDR practitioners. The potential consequences for helping professionals working with traumatized clients are examined with a description of signs and symptoms of secondary trauma. Preventative measures that can be taken by the individual and the organization in which he or she works are explored, and current recommendations for treatment options are outlined. Readers may wish to complete the action plan in Resource 7.1 as they go through this chapter.

CATHERINE'S STORY (PART 1)

I walked out of work today. It was dark and foggy, and it all felt quite surreal as I filled my car with books, certificates, and personal items from my office. My colleague Sam helped me load the car and his look of concern remains with me.

    We both know I'm not going back, and we both can't quite believe it. As a team leader, I feel like I'm abandoning my colleagues but I just can't do this anymore. I've become a shadow of myself, always negative and on guard. I dread new clients arriving—more work—and say a silent prayer of thanks at last-minute cancellations. The stories I hear are increasingly staying with me, pictures of dead children, mutilated bodies, and death. I'm not alone. When I look at my team I see signs of secondary trauma—hyperarousal, numbing with alcohol, cynicism, irritability, and bouts of tearfulness—but nobody of any influence, nobody who can make a difference to our intense workload and long hours, is interested. We have to fight for everything, even clinical supervision.

    I'm voting with my feet for the sake of my sanity and my family. They deserve better than this. I trained long and hard to get to where I was and now it's all gone. I don't think I can ever do this work again and feel such a failure. My future looks bleak.

Secondary trauma is costly. The cost to individual therapists and their families, such as the example of Catherine and her team, is incalculable as are the cost to clients of a less-than-healthy practitioner. The cost to the employing organization is high with increased turnover, sickness absence, and reduced productivity. There is the potential for a reduced standard in service and complaints. While the risks are high, a complex mix of factors determines the impact of secondary traumatic stress on the practitioner. Each therapeutic situation is unique with an interaction between situational factors and the helper's response to it. The nature of EMDR brings another dimension to the mix.

HELPER'S RESPONSE TO WORKING WITH TRAUMA

Earlier chapters described how our belief system permeates through every aspect of our lives and helps us to create our identity. When we become therapists, we bring these fundamental assumptions to our professional identity, for example, "the world is just and makes sense" and "I am basically a good person." However, because we are repeatedly

---

Case Example
Susan's Story

Since working in the rape crisis center, I've definitely noticed a change in how I feel about my own safety. Some of this was good, I suppose, to begin with—a general increase in awareness of potentially dangerous situations—but I'm beginning to worry that it's giving me a skewed perspective on life and on men, in particular. I'm aware that there are so many bad people about. I'm less trusting and more watchful, and I think this had made me a less open, more negative person. I don't like that about myself.

---

exposed to the horrors of trauma and the effects on survivors, these assumptions may be shattered leading to secondary trauma. Disruptions in the psychological need areas of safety, trust, esteem, power, and intimacy may occur and these are reflected in the signs and symptoms of secondary trauma.

> Survivors of extreme events are threatening...because of the more subtle, yet potent threat they pose to our fundamental assumptions, core beliefs that enable us to feel safe, secure, and confident. Survivors of extreme events are powerful reminders of human frailty and the fact that the world can be malevolent, callous and cruel. (Janoff-Bulman, 1985, p. 148)

When we work with trauma we are therefore confronted with our own mortality and vulnerability and must adapt and build up our own defenses against this pain. Extreme defenses can include cynicism and indifference. Paul Valent (1995) proposed that we respond to trauma with survival strategies (SSs). "For helpers, rescuing and asserting are commonly used SSs. So when not coping, helpers may come to feel, respectively, burdened, resentful, rejecting, and guilty; and frustrated, demoralized, not in control, exhausted and burned out." (Valent, 1995, p. 45).

Additional factors such as transference can be a risk, for example, clients who have suffered harm at the hands of others may perceive the therapist as controlling or abusive. Countertransference and identification in the therapeutic relationship can also take their toll on the therapist's core beliefs. Although it is helpful for the therapist to identify with and understand the client's experience, this is a double-edged sword

SURVIVAL STRATEGIES	SUCCESSFUL/ ADAPTIVE RESPONSE	UNSUCCESSFUL/MALADAPTIVE RESPONSE		TRAUMA RESPONSE
		PSYCHOLOGICAL	SOCIAL	
Rescuing	Care Empathy Nurture	Resentment Depletion Self-concern	Burden Neglect Rejection	Anguish Guilt
Asserting	Potency Success Control	Frustration Low morale Powerlessness	Willfulness Failure Lost control	Burnout

Adapted from Valent (1995).

where the therapist overly identifies with the client, maybe through having a similar history. Empathy is one of the therapist's major resources when working with trauma, but it is also a key factor in the transmission of traumatic material from client to helper.

By empathizing we can better understand clients but also better feel, and absorb, their distress. In her book "Help for the Helper," Rothschild (2006) described the brain mechanisms that operate in interpersonal empathy and emphasized the need for tools that increase our awareness and reduce our vulnerabilities to secondary trauma. Unconscious empathy operates outside of the therapist's awareness and we naturally mirror people with whom we are in close communication. For the therapist working with traumatized clients, this can mean we—consciously or unconsciously—mimic expressions and posture. Rothschild explains

Case Example
Sam's Story

I used to get wiped out by a particular client who I was working long term with on childhood trauma. Now when I notice my levels of arousal rising during a session, such as my breathing changing, feeling tense or sweaty, I concentrate on pulling back and observing the situation almost as a third party in the room. What I would describe as my own dual focus—observing the client's nonverbal signals and words—rather than deeply empathizing, stepping into their shoes, as I was previously. I used to feel that if I wasn't feeling their pain then I wasn't caring. Now I know that I can be a better therapist by maintaining that distance when appropriate.

how we have somatic markers that will elicit reactions in ourselves. For instance, the upturned mouth of a smile will elicit a happy feeling. This is the afferent feedback system (body to brain) of the nervous system. However, mirroring a distressed client's expression or posture, such as frowning, down turned mouth, hunched posture, can trigger the relevant somatic markers in the therapist. This has a negative impact.

"(A)dopting an empathic facial expression or posture with your client—consciously or unconsciously—can dramatically affect you." (Rothschild, 2006, p. 41)

As we naturally match the person we are in close contact with, by changes to our breathing and heart rate, for example, even our client's levels of arousal can be picked up unconsciously. This is used consciously by many therapists to good effect. Taking a calming breath and relaxing subtly will often have a noticeable effect on a client's anxiety. The opposite is true, however, and the raised heart rate and shallow breathing of a client can be unconsciously matched by the therapist. In extreme cases, therapists may catch themselves holding their breath as clients recount details of their trauma.

Rothschild further described how mirror neurons add to this effect. Mirror neurons are brain cells that reflect the activity of another's brain cells. When we observe behavior, it is as though we are actually doing/feeling that. This can explain the feeling of having absorbed the client's experience and distress.

Working in close proximity will exacerbate all these matching and mirroring effects and Rothschild emphasized the need for therapists to

---

Case Example
Jim's Story

I do find that the physically close-up nature of a desensitization session is demanding. Being so close to a client who is in a great deal of distress, I feel like I am sitting in a pool of negative energy sometimes, and it's a relief to get back to my chair and create some distance at the end of desensitization. That level of physical intimacy alongside the intense work is draining.

> ### Case Example
> ### James' Story
>
> I sometimes find it really helpful when I'm assessing the target image to get a feel for that memory. I do sit in the client's chair at that point (not literally!) and have found by associating myself with the image I can better help my client identify negative cognitions and emotions and have even picked up on my client's bodily sensations. Sometimes I get a sensation, for example, that a negative cognition doesn't fit, and I can check this out with my client and am surprisingly accurate. I always make sure I'm not imposing my beliefs or experience on the client though.
>
> This is a double-edged sword, however, and I can find some target images are particularly vivid. In these cases, I have to step back out into impartial observer. I am aware I have to be extra careful that this association with the image myself is done consciously and is limited.

be aware of their personal space and comfort zone. This can quite literally separate the therapist from the client's experience. The nature of EMDR often requires us to have close proximity with our clients, therefore increasing the physical matching described above.

The imagery system of memory is the most likely to be affected by trauma (Paivio, 1986 cited in Figley, 1995). The impact of the "hot spot" target memory and its associated imagery can feel like sharing the client's worst bit, and some therapists may find themselves standing in their client's shoes as they work through the assessment and desensitization phases.

SITUATIONAL FACTORS IN THE DEVELOPMENT OF SECONDARY TRAUMA

Several factors are identified in the literature as increasing the risk for therapist.

The Nature and Intensity of Workload

It is common sense that the more exposure to traumatic material, the more the therapist will be affected. Having a balance of cases and

Case Example
Mandy's Story

I was really excited about doing my EMDR training. I completed level 2 last year and am the only EMDR trained clinician in the charitable counseling agency where I work. Unfortunately, that means that I'm now given all the complex cases to work with. It seems like whenever we get a case of trauma, especially individuals with PTSD, it's automatically assumed I'll take it on. My workload hasn't increased but I get colleagues coming to me all the time asking me to take on their clients who "really need EMDR" and I'm conscious of my waiting list growing. I guess that in itself puts some pressure on, but the hardest thing is that all I'm working with now is complicated trauma. I no longer do any general counseling and support which, to be honest, used to provide some respite at work. There's no sign of anyone else doing the training but now I don't always look forward to going to work, and I was never like that before.

limiting the number of clients seen in a week or on a particular day is ideal. As EMDR therapists, we are more likely to be working with cases of trauma and therefore our core beliefs are at greater risk of being challenged.

Poor Support Mechanisms

While encouraging our clients to mobilize their support networks, therapists can be reluctant to acknowledge their own need for help. We are the "fixers and copers," the ones who others come to. Our need for this sense of competence sometimes does not allow us to seek support. Support should come from family, friends, colleagues, peers, and managers. Acknowledging that secondary trauma is a reality and that we are all at risk is crucial.

Supervision Access and Appropriateness

Again it is common sense that we are less likely to feel negatively impacted by our work if we feel well trained and competent. Less-experienced therapists are more vulnerable to secondary trauma. Clinical supervision provides much of our own safety net, reducing our isolation and helping

Case Example
Robert's Story

I was trained in EMDR at the same time as my three colleagues, but we seem to have taken different messages from the course. I was left with the impression of EMDR as a very powerful technique to be used with caution and, as a very conscientious person anyway, I really want to be sure I'm not doing harm to my clients. I take a long time on preparation and making sure my client is ready and willing for reprocessing.

My colleagues came away from the course like they had a new toy. They're just running with it and keen to use it on everyone. So far, they've had some good cases, but I do feel they're being a bit overzealous. I'm scared of doing something wrong and am feeling increasingly disempowered and incompetent. It wouldn't be so bad if they weren't at the other end of the spectrum. I feel like a slow learner and I know this is down to my cautious style, but even my manager is dropping hints that perhaps I should be doing more. It seems like such a big change to my practice that I need time to integrate it and build my confidence. I'd quite like to join a peer support group as I don't feel like I can ask questions of my colleagues without them telling me to "just have a go."

Case Example
Yvonne's Story

I've been in private practice for 6 years and thought EMDR would be an additional tool to use with my (mainly) trauma clients. I was flying when I came away from the course, really excited about what I could offer and I have to say for the first few months things were great with some good successes. I've had a couple of clients lately though who've had abreactions and blocks and feel like I'm losing my confidence. My clinical supervisor is not trained in EMDR and is quite skeptical about it. I've noticed I'm reluctant to bring these cases to supervision as I fear her criticism. She's a great supervisor otherwise but just doesn't like EMDR, so I don't want to change and can't really afford two supervisors.

us to manage difficulties in the process, but in many areas EMDR supervision can be scarce.

Secondary trauma is an occupational hazard for all therapists, but EMDR practitioners need to be especially aware. The constructs for these psychological injuries are now detailed along with their main signs and symptoms. It should be remembered that they are *not* signs of weakness but a risk of the necessary work that we are all committed to.

CONCEPTUAL FRAMEWORK

Compassion Fatigue and Secondary Traumatic Stress Disorder

Compassion stress is the natural outcome that can result from knowing about trauma experienced by a client, friend, or family member. CF arises when this normal stress becomes longer term or debilitating. In the literature, CF is sometimes used as a generic term for the strains of being in a helping role. Secondary Traumatic Stress Disorder (STSD) is synonymous with CF and described as "the natural consequent behaviors and emotion resulting from knowing about a traumatizing event experienced by a significant other—the stress resulting from helping or wanting to help a traumatized or suffering person" (Figley, 1995, p. 7).

Signs and symptoms of CF/STSD are wide ranging and mirror those of PTSD:

- Physical: sleep disruption and physiological response to trauma triggers
- Cognitive: avoidance of thoughts associated with the trauma, intrusive trauma-related thoughts, sense of a foreshortened future, reexperiencing of the traumatic event or traumatized person, difficulties concentrating, and nightmares
- Behavioral: avoidance of trauma-related activities, detachment from others, hypervigilance, exaggerated startle response, and reduced interest in pleasure-giving activities
- Emotional: numbing, irritability, efforts to avoid trauma-related feelings.

Vicarious Trauma

As stated earlier, when therapists empathize deeply with a client, their beliefs are challenged and cognitive disruptions can occur. VT is the result of this disruption and is described as "the transformation in the inner experience of the therapist that comes about as a result of the empathic engagement with clients' trauma material" (Pearlman & Saakvitne, 1995, p. 31).

Signs and symptoms of VT include

- Physical: feeling unsafe, intrusive sensory material relating to traumatic events, and exhaustion
- Cognitive: questioning self-beliefs around competence, worthiness, trust, being loved, having a right to be happy/alive, poor decision making, and cynicism
- Behavioral: social disconnection, bouts of tearfulness or anger, and avoidance of trauma-related triggers
- Emotional: feeling overwhelmed, frustrated, anxious or emotionally numb, despair, and resentful.

Burnout

Burnout is a concept that is equally applicable to other kinds of professionals and is characterized by deterioration in physical and mental health as a result of the intensity and quantity of work. Burnout has been described as "a state of physical, emotional and mental exhaustion caused by long term involvement in emotionally demanding situations" (Pines & Aronson, 1988, p. 9).

Symptoms of burnout include:

- Physical: headaches, chronic fatigue, frequent and prolonged colds, exacerbated preexisting physical disorders, sleep disturbance, and sudden weight gain or loss
- Cognitive: negativity and cynicism, and feeling trapped and isolated
- Behavioral: increase in maladaptive strategies such as alcohol and other stimulants, risk-taking behavior, and poor work performance
- Emotional: hopelessness and depression, anger and disillusionment, and helplessness.

INTERVENTIONS

Whenever considering measures to address secondary trauma, it is important to consider all the parts of the jigsaw including situational factors, the individual therapist, and the special dimension that EMDR can bring. Interventions can be grouped into three categories (personal, professional, organizational), but it is important to consider the whole picture. No matter how good one category is, it can be negated by problems in the others. For example, even therapists with the best personal care in the world will be affected if they work in an environment that undermines and overloads them. There are several self-reporting scales that measure the effects of secondary trauma, and Resource 7.2 details some of these. It can be useful to monitor levels regularly, perhaps 6 monthly or so, and discuss with a supervisor or trusted colleague.

Personal Interventions

The better we take care of ourselves, the healthier we are and the better we can serve our clients. A balance between work life and personal life is needed, but this is something that has to be constantly strived for. Our emotional, physical, spiritual, and community/social needs all need to be considered.

The following questions are worth asking on a regular basis:

- Do I eat regular, healthy meals and minimize junk food?
- Do I take regular exercise, raising my heart rate and getting my lungs working?
- Do I have time for "me" when I can participate in hobbies or interests?
- Do I practice mindfulness?
- Do I have a going home ritual so that I leave the workplace behind?
- Do I have at least one alcohol-free day per week and keep within my safe drinking levels at other times?
- Do I have quiet time when I physically and mentally relax completely?
- Do I take regular short breaks within my working day, particularly for lunch and between clients?
- Do I have people in my life who can listen to me and do I talk to them? When did I last speak to them?

- Do I have fun? When was the last time?
- Do I spend time in nature?
- Do I know how to say "No" and do I actually say it when appropriate?

Chapter Resource 7.3: Healing Activities can give you some ideas. Try a new one every week, add your own activities and share ideas with colleagues.

Sometimes we do not notice changes until we are becoming quite debilitated. Personal psychotherapy and EMDR (Keenan & Royle, 2008) can be useful in tackling the disrupted schemas of secondary trauma. Sensory-based therapy as described by Chrys J. Harris aims to help trauma workers to answer "What happened? Why did it happen? Why did I act as I did then? Why have I acted as I have since then? What will I do if it happens again?" (Figley, 1995, p. 113).

Professional Interventions

As a novice EMDR practitioner it may be interesting to pay attention to your self-talk before, during, or after sessions. How you judge your own competency can have a big effect. Be aware of negative self-talk such as

I can't do this... It's all going wrong... I don't know how to handle this... That session was awful... I really messed up...

Ongoing supervision in EMDR after completing training will be of great benefit in building a sense of confidence and competence.

Case Example
Carol's Story

I take my self-care very seriously. I work hard to manage my workload—sometimes I'm more successful than others. I go running and have just started a salsa dancing class—a great balance to trauma work!

One thing that I've found helpful after a heavy session is to use EMDR on myself. I have a machine that uses tapping for bilateral stimulation, and 5 min of this generally has a calming effect on me and does help me settle down.

Case Example
Wendy's Story

As a counselor working within a small mental health team based in the community setting, I trained in EMDR and was excited about incorporating this into my casework. However, I can't access EMDR supervision, there's just no vacancy with anyone within traveling distance. My colleagues not only don't understand EMDR but also are quite threatened and negative about it.

I initially had some success with a couple of clients but lately I've had a few problems and my own confidence in EMDR, and even in myself as a practitioner, is draining away. I'm thinking of going back to my old techniques leaving the EMDR for a little while.

Continuous professional development, training, workshops, and conferences, not only have this effect but also allow us to network and meet other EMDR therapists, potentially building up our social support. It can be quite isolating working as an EMDR therapist, and belonging to a peer group can make a big difference.

Case Example
Gary's Story

I had given up with EMDR and quite by chance got talking to a practitioner from my town at a trauma conference who told me she was using EMDR successfully. Her enthusiasm was contagious, and I was encouraged to join a local interest group. I hadn't been aware of its existence as I wasn't a member of the national EMDR association, but I have to say it's been great. The first few times I went along I still wasn't practicing EMDR, but I began to hear about some cases that had similar problems to my own earlier work. Hearing ideas from the group about how to tackle these made me rethink my own practice, and I began to reintroduce EMDR to this. Having this peer support and the acknowledgment that it doesn't always go smoothly has been fantastic. I think that after my training I was expecting EMDR to be a magic wand and wasn't prepared for the obstacles. Now I meet them as challenges and am learning loads from my peers.

Embarking on the route to accreditation as an EMDR practitioner builds skills and provides a real sense of professional competence. The accreditation criteria may seem intimidating but can be easily achieved with determination, application, and good supervision.

Issues such as privacy and comfort in the consulting room are important. Where rooms are shared it can be more difficult to create your own safe place but, if you have your own room, think about clearing the clutter and having grounding objects, plants, and inspirational pictures. Reminders of why you are doing this work, such as thank you letters and cards from old clients can be kept and leafed through when you are feeling ineffective or stuck with a client.

Organizational Interventions

The organization in which the EMDR therapist works has a responsibility to minimize the risk of secondary trauma by:

- Providing a suitable environment for the work with attention to privacy and comfort
- Creating a respectful environment
- Providing adequate resources for Continuous Professional Development, staff cover, and clinical supervision
- Managing workloads in terms of number and intensity of cases—this is usually reliant on sufficient levels of employees being present
- Ensuring that staff support is in place and that professional guidelines are adhered to
- Acknowledging secondary trauma as an occupational hazard
- Actively encouraging therapist self-care.

CATHERINE'S STORY (PART 2)

It took me a couple of years to fully recover from that time in my life. For about 6 months I didn't work. I suffered from depression and anxiety and questioned everything about my life. However, with the support of some good friends and determination on my part, I rebuilt my career and am now practising therapy again in a much healthier environment. I have supervision, ongoing training, time to read journals and keep up to date in my field and, most importantly for me, a realistic workload. I appreciate the signs of secondary trauma and monitor my levels taking remedial action when needed. I'm happy in my work and, with every success my clients and I achieve, I celebrate that I got out while I was still able to. I now practice what I preach and am better able to help my clients.

LEARNING SUMMARY

You should feel confident that you are able to:

- Identify the risk factors associated with secondary traumatic stress
- Recognize the signs and symptoms of distress in yourself and colleagues
- Put in place measures to reduce the impact of working with traumatized individuals
- Take care of yourself when the going gets tough.

Make a personal commitment to yourself and your work—you are both very important.

RESOURCES

7.1: My Action Plan

The main vulnerabilities in my work context:

Signs and symptoms I have noticed:

Actions I can take in my personal life to address the risks of VT:

Actions I can take in my professional life to address the risks of VT:

Actions I can suggest to my organization or manager:

7.2: Secondary Trauma Scales and Inventories

Secondary Trauma Questionnaire (Stamm, 2002)
Traumatic Stress Institute Life Orientation Inventory URL: http://www.tsicaap.com
Secondary Traumatic Stress Scale (Bride, Robinson, Yegidis, & Figley, 2003)
Traumatic Stress Institute Belief Scale (Adams Betts, Matto, & Harrington, 2001)

Burnout Potential Inventory (Potter, 1998)
Maslach Burnout Inventory (Maslach, Jackson, & Schwab, 1996)
Oldenburg Burnout Inventory (Demerouti, Bakker, Vardakou, & Kantas, 2003).

7.3: Healing Activities

Take a warm bubble bath
Have breakfast in bed and read the newspapers at leisure
Take a sauna
Get a massage
Walk in a park and feed the ducks
Visit a zoo
Have a manicure or a pedicure
Stop and smell some flowers
Watch the sunrise or sunset
Relax with a good book and/or soothing music
Rent a funny movie
Play your favorite music and dance to it by yourself
Go to bed early
Call a good friend—or several good friends
Make yourself a nice meal by candlelight
Go to the beach and paddle in the waves
Take a scenic drive
Meditate
Wear something that you normally save for "best"
Browse in a book store for as long as you want
Hug someone
Buy yourself something special that you can afford
Go and see a good film or show
Go to the park and swing on the swings
Visit a museum or a gallery
Work on your favorite puzzle book
Buy an affirmation tape or inspirational book
Do a jigsaw
Write a letter to an old friend
Help out in your local community
Go window shopping
Exercise
Do something outrageous—but legal!

Appendix A: Theoretical Background to the Adaptive Information Processing Model

Before commencing desensitization, the therapist should have a good understanding of how memory networks are created, how the AIP model works and, based on client presentation, should be able to develop a targeting sequence plan using the three-pronged approach to treatment.

This introduction offers a broad overview of these areas and a reminder of the theoretical underpinning of EMDR, all of which will be detailed further in the relevant chapters throughout the book.

CLIENT PRESENTATIONS

EMDR is an integrative psychotherapeutic approach and as such, it is important to be aware that any case conceptualization is always done within a comprehensive treatment plan. The goal of EMDR is to maintain client safety while achieving the most effective and efficient recovery. From the first meeting, and throughout therapy, the clinician should monitor the client's stability and pay careful consideration to his or her ability to manage stress. The client needs self-regulation skills to manage both external and internal challenges during therapy. This is important not only in processing but also in history taking so as not to swamp or overwhelm the client. The depth and comprehensiveness of history taking will be determined by the client's internal and external resources (e.g., stability, emotional regulation, affect tolerance, social supports). As with any other therapy, early attachment history and the clients' sense of safety in childhood should be considered when deciding on the pace and depth of history taking. Progression can vary from straightforward questioning when people are relatively resourced to a slower paced, gentler approach. This may involve only exploring current daily functioning, anxieties, and issues. Some clients may need stabilization and skills building before taking a full history or developing an EMDR targeting sequence plan. Using your clinical judgment is a key skill within the process of EMDR.

Clients will present on a continuum of complexity as to their history. At the "simpler" end is the client presenting with symptoms following a single incident. This may have happened recently resulting in the client experiencing a set of symptoms directly related to that event or an acute stress response.

Clients may present with a series of events that are organized around one dominant theme represented by a single symptom, such as a core negative belief, pervasive emotional state, frequent body sensation, and pattern of behavior. This may be the result of small "t" events from early childhood experiences.

Following assessment, it may be determined that the client has PTSD following an event or a series of events over a prolonged period. The origin of this may be in adulthood or early childhood experiences.

Toward the more complex end of the continuum, clients may have multiple issues and symptoms including depression, anxiety, panic reactions, problems with relationships, some dissociative processes, low self-esteem, and less severe characterological issues. It may be that numerous memories over time have produced the pathology, but the client does not meet the full diagnostic criteria for PTSD.

Some clients have a complex presentation of traumatic life events and extreme stress over a prolonged period of time. Symptoms may include more severe personality and dissociative phenomena. Much more preparation is required for such clients, and therapists should wait until completing EMDR training and having undertaken specialty training in the fields of complex trauma and dissociation.

Many clients will have come to therapy in a state of crisis. They may have been suffering for some time with symptoms, and a "final straw" results in overwhelm and chaos. An acute presentation requires caution and case consultation, particularly for the novice practitioner. All clients should be screened for DD and the clinician should be sensitive to previous or current.

- Life-threatening substance abuse
- Serious suicide attempts
- Self-harm such as cutting, parasuicide acts
- Serious violence to others or property

MEMORY NETWORKS

When clients enter the consulting room, they bring their own unique experiences, beliefs, and perceptions with them. When clinically appropriate, the therapist will gather the information necessary for EMDR case conceptualization and for targeting sequence planning. To do this, the therapist needs to have an understanding of memory networks and how information is stored.

Our experience of life is stored as memories. These experiences are made up of stored sensory input, for example, the images, sounds, tastes, and smells associated with the event. This information may be stored with associated thoughts, beliefs, and feelings as well as with body sensations.

An example of this may be the memory of spending time with a beloved grandparent. Elsa remembers sitting in her grandmother's kitchen while she baked bread. The smell of freshly baked bread invokes this memory and its feeing of well-being. When she accesses this memory, she becomes relaxed and believes herself to be lovable and safe. She can remember the bright colors of her grandmother's apron and the feeling of the rough wooden table. This memory is adaptively stored and contributes to her self-esteem.

Memories with similar information are linked by their channels of association and stored in memory networks. As well as sensory data, association may be made by links with thoughts, emotions, body sensations, and beliefs. Memory networks form the basis of our perceptions, attitudes, and behaviors. They can be considered as the blocks with which we construct the world, how we feel about later events and ourselves and may be adaptive or maladaptive.

Adaptive memory networks are the primary basis of our learning, self-esteem, positive growth, and adaptive resources and behaviors. During the preparation phase, the therapist may wish to add or enhance access to these positive networks through, for example, resource installation or safe place enhancement.

However, not all memories are stored adaptively. EMDR theory posits that maladaptive or dysfunctional memory networks are the primary basis of pathology. Memories are considered "dysfunctional" because they are physiologically stored in a way that does not allow them to link to any positive/adaptive networks.

Consequently, memory networks are viewed as the underlying basis of clinical symptoms and mental health and are the foundation of the EMDR approach. High levels of disturbing emotions may cause disruptions, which, in turn, can prevent experiences from being adaptively processed. As such, EMDR is a psychotherapy approach (distinct from other therapeutic models) that is guided by an information processing model, which is independent of any particular neurobiological mechanism.

ADAPTIVE INFORMATION PROCESSING

The AIP model (Shapiro, 2001) has many components and is a physical information processing system, which, like any other body system, has a natural tendency to be guided toward well-being. For example, a cut closes and heals unless it is infected. Similarly, with emotions, when we experience a distressing event, over time, the information processing system unhooks the disturbing emotions, thoughts, physical sensations connected to an event, resulting in adaptive resolution, thus constructing functional memories and memory networks.

However, if there is a blockage in the information processing system, the result is disturbing memories, which are dysfunctionally stored as they were perceived at the time of the event, with the associated emotions, physical sensations, thoughts, and beliefs. These can be readily triggered in the present. This is thought to be due to the connection between the past and the present, which the individual is not able to differentiate. The perceptions of current situations link into the networks of physically stored memories to be interpreted. Consequently, if a memory network contains an unprocessed memory, the current perceptions are formed by the earlier unsettling emotions, thoughts, beliefs, and physical sensations of the past event.

Shapiro (2001) posits that reprocessing is the forging of adaptive associations between networks of information stored in the brain. EMDR facilitates an associative process that allows the relevant connections to be made. The unprocessed components or manifestations of memory (image, thoughts, sounds, emotions, physical sensations, and beliefs) transform during processing to an adaptive resolution. What is useful is stored, available to inform future experiences, and what is no longer adaptive is discarded (for example, physical sensations, irrational beliefs). To summarize, EMDR procedures activate the target memory and stimulate the AIP system. As a result, negative and/or disturbing memories are reprocessed, and positive memories are integrated.

During the phase of reprocessing, the maladaptive/dysfunctional memory networks start to link with existing positive, adaptive and functional memory networks. Accessing experiences (positive and negative) allows for the linkages between consciousness and where information is stored. EMDR-activated reprocessing is metaphorically like moving down a train track toward a more adaptive/functional resolution. Each stop allows linkage to existing adaptive positive networks.

As a result of EMDR-activated adaptive information reprocessing, emotional and physical disturbance is desensitized. Furthermore, there is an emergence of insight and positive changes in physical and emotional responses. Consequently, this culminates in integration, when the new learning becomes available in the current life situation.

However, positive memory networks need to be present and accessible for reprocessing to occur. Resource development and improvement of existing resources is an important part of this process. This is done by accessing positive life experiences and adaptive memories (senses, thoughts, emotions, physical sensation, beliefs), which are then strengthened and enhanced through the addition of dual attention stimulus. It is important to note that the therapeutic relationship can also create a positive memory network.

CASE CONCEPTUALIZATION

Working in collaboration with the client, the aim of EMDR is to achieve appropriate, adaptive, and natural resolution of presenting problems and to incorporate new skills, behaviors, and beliefs about the self, ultimately this increases the client's capacity to respond adaptively in the current context of their lives. Within the comprehensive eight-phase protocol, the therapist and client should collaboratively develop a targeting sequence plan consistent with the client's treatment goals. Attention should be paid to a choice of targets that will fill in developmental deficits and move the client to a more adaptive and healthy present.

According to the *AIP* model, present reactions can be traced to past experiences that have set the groundwork for pathology. Current symptoms are caused by earlier experiences that were not adequately processed due to trauma or insufficient, adaptive information.

As part of the targeted sequencing plan, symptom clusters should be identified. They may include instances of associated irrational negative beliefs, emotions, people, places or things, body sensations, and other sensory data (e.g., smell, sound). In EMDR, the negative belief is viewed as a verbalization of the stored affect. The self bases a belief on the sense of the memory, and this resonates with the affect. Dominant irrational beliefs can provide a thread through the individual's life. When a negative belief presents itself as a pervasive theme or symptom, it is often useful to organize the targeting sequence plan around that negative core belief.

With memories that are stored in dysfunctional memory networks, the touchstone memory needs to be identified. The touchstone memory is the earliest recalled experience that laid the foundation for the client's presenting problem. The assessment phase of EMDR will consider the aspects of this memory such as the negative belief, emotion, and body sensation. The node is the memory designated for therapeutic targeting. It is a biologically stored experience, which represents a memory network.

THE THREE-PRONGED APPROACH

The three-pronged approach identifies specific targets for reprocessing—past, present, and future.

- Past memories or etiological incidents should be identified that appear to have set the pathology in process. Present reactions and symptoms can be linked to past memories or other experiential contributors. As well as the first experience (touchstone memory), the worst experience and other contributing experiences should be identified.
- Present situations that exacerbate the dysfunction and cause disturbing symptoms and reactions should be identified along with any current triggers that remain due to second-order conditioning.
- The client's positive vision and desired future responses are identified. The therapist should consider the potential challenges that could occur along with any skills deficit and more adaptive set of responses to be developed and acted upon.

Each presenting complaint is then targeted in this order of past, present, and future.

Ongoing reevaluation of the treatment plan and targeting sequence strategies may be necessary as treatment evolves. Particularly when working with complex cases, it can be all too easy to lose sight of the wood for the trees. Take time to step back regularly and review the plan, and progress, with the client.

Appendix B: The Eight Phases of the EMDR Standard Protocol

It is important to remember that EMDR is a distinct eight-phase integrative treatment approach and, as such, each step of the protocol has a clinical purpose. Studies that have maintained fidelity to the EMDR protocol have demonstrated largest treatment effect (Maxfield & Hyer, 2002).

PHASE ONE: HISTORY TAKING

Information is gathered to ascertain client appropriateness for EMDR treatment. This will include taking the client's history, determining the current level of functioning along with goals for therapy, safety factors, and selection of targets for processing.

PHASE TWO: PREPARATION

In this phase, the therapeutic relationship is being built and a clear explanation of EMDR given. Client fears and expectations are addressed, a safe place and/or other positive memory networks are established, and eye movements or other form of DAS are tested. It is during this phase that the clinician establishes the client's capacity to maintain dual awareness between the past and the present. In addition, time should be taken to develop and enhance affect management skills to ensure the client is able to shift states comfortably.

PHASE THREE: ASSESSMENT

Assessment is the third phase of the EMDR protocol during which the components of the target memory are elicited in a structured way in collaboration with the client, thus establishing the baseline measures to determine the client's response to desensitization and to activate the memory the client will be reprocessing.

PHASE FOUR: DESENSITIZATION

The effect of desensitization is to reduce the disturbance related to the target memory and associated cues by reprocessing the memory, which then activates related channels of association. SUDS are used to measure the treatment effect.

PHASE FIVE: INSTALLATION

The installation phase is concerned with reevaluating the suitability and then integrating the positive cognition with the targeted memory, resulting in strengthening and enhancing associations to positive memory networks. This would only be done after desensitization is complete.

PHASE SIX: BODY SCAN

The therapist will assess adaptive resolution of the target by asking the client to hold the original memory, while considering the positive cognition, and checking his or her body for any tension or sensation. The therapist should then target any residual physical manifestation with DAS.

PHASE SEVEN: CLOSURE

During this phase (if the session is incomplete) clients' emotional state is stabilized and they are *reoriented* to the present. They are fully debriefed and advised to keep a log.

PHASE EIGHT: REEVALUATION

Reevaluation is the eighth phase of EMDR. Reevaluation is done at the beginning of each session following a desensitization session. It involves reevaluating the general level of function in addition to reviewing the client's journal, assessing the current state of the previously targeted material, and considering the subsequent targets and treatment plan.

Appendix C: Further Information and Advice

The Journal of EMDR Practice and Research:
  http://springerjournals.com

Useful websites:
EMDR International Association (EMDRIA): www.emdria.org
EMDR Institute: www.emdr.com
EMDR Europe: www.emdr-europe.org
EMDR UK & Ireland: www.emdrassociation.org
International Society for Traumatic Stress Studies: www.istss.org
European Society for Traumatic Stress Studies: www.estss.org
EMDR Humanitarian Assistance Programs: www.emdrhap.org
International Society for the Study of Trauma and Dissociation:
  www.isst-d.org

Appendix D: Clients' Experiences of EMDR: In Their Own Words

When therapists are feeling consciously incompetent and trying hard to integrate EMDR into their existing skills and knowledge, they can lose sight of why they embarked on this steep learning curve. When the going gets tough it is worth remembering what we are striving for and why certain aspects are important. Sometimes clients express what is important better than the "professionals" can and, in this chapter, individuals who have experienced EMDR for a range of problems share some of their experiences in their own words.

GOALS AND EXPECTATIONS

Clients present with a range of goals and expectations. It is important to explore and define these and to reevaluate goals as the therapy progresses. Some clients are unsure whether EMDR will be able to help them but are nevertheless hopeful. Expectations run along a continuum, from wanting a magic wand or quick fix to having no expectations at all. Some clients will have specific goals, others just a vague feeling of needing something to change or improve.

> I entered into EMDR with an open mind. I wanted to be able to go to the dentist without fear and had avoided this previously for many years despite bad toothache. I can't really answer whether I expected it to work or not. I hoped it would work. When I knew what was going to happen I was very skeptical. To be honest, I couldn't see how it would help.
>
> In terms of what I initially wanted from EMDR, my first thought was to feel well again, to live my life again—to be normal and not abnormal. I didn't know just what to expect.

REASONS FOR CHOOSING EMDR

Compared with other therapeutic approaches, EMDR is a relatively lesser known therapy. Clients may be recommended for EMDR, the therapist working with the client may recognize that EMDR could be helpful, or clients themselves may have done quite a bit of research before deciding on their choice of therapy. Reasons for choosing EMDR include a desire to let go of the rational, logical self and to be able to engage at a deeper level. Some clients want to understand and deal with the root cause of their problems rather than work on symptom management.

> I am so grateful that my therapist recognized the root cause of my depression and fears was from trauma. When I initially did some research into EMDR it seemed that it was aimed mainly at victims of what one might call "severe trauma," for example, victims of abuse and war, and firefighters or police, but I didn't quite get the sense that I might fit into a category that might warrant my experiences worthy of EMDR therapy. Yet, without EMDR, I feel I would still be rationalizing, thinking things through, aware of how my previous experiences might have shaped me, but never truly moving forward emotionally.

PREPARATION AND HISTORY TAKING

The importance of taking time in the early phases of EMDR has been constantly reinforced throughout this book to ensure that later desensitization is optimized. Working transparently and empowering the client gives him or her a sense of control and collaboration in the process. As the client may not retain all the information provided in sessions, explanations should be clear and simple.

> My therapist explained every step of the way, what we were doing *together*. She never ever pushed me into anything I didn't want to do. It was also really useful that she explained it in simple terms. If I can recall it was described as visiting situations in time that I felt were traumatic, seeing it, feeling it, but always with the reassurance that it was a memory, the past … and therefore being in a safe place in which to explore my feelings around those events.

CLIENT ANXIETY

The best preparation in the world will not always fully address client's anxiety about desensitization. The stop signal gives the client an important sense of control. Equally important are the reassurance and support provided by the therapist.

> I suppose it really was basically a fear of the unknown and perhaps a sense of dread re-visiting memories I had done my utmost to avoid for so many years. However, I somehow knew that everything I had read about EMDR and what my counselor had told me was the way forward for me.
>
> I suppose I was anxious about the process, yet excited about the effect at the same time.

DESENSITIZATION EXPERIENCE

Each individual has his or her own unique experience during desensitization, and clinicians rely on the feedback provided during this phase. Clients can still be surprised at the power of EMDR despite the amount of preparation that is done and can still experience strong emotions. Conversely, they may be disappointed because it is not what they expected or they may almost feel a sense of anticlimax that it was not as bad as expected.

> My first EMDR session involved quickly revisiting a series of traumatic events from my past. Initially, I felt that my most traumatic moment was in recovery after an operation on my face. I was able to see, feel, almost relive the emotions that I had at the time ... the horror, the uncertainty, the pain, but throughout the session and at the end I was able to look at it objectively and understand it all for what it really was. I cried. Probably, the first time I had cried properly in years. I cried for me, my family, and all the years that I had let that part of my life cripple me emotionally. What I hadn't expected was that it also brought up memories of other events around the same time, which had contributed to this being so traumatic for me. I felt guilt since a year before my operation my Mum had died, and I knew from my tears that I hadn't let myself grieve properly because of being so self-absorbed with my operation and my reaction afterwards.
>
> (It was) liberating, at times terrifying, all consuming much of the time, better than any detective novel so revealing, exciting, and rewarding.

MAKING CONNECTIONS AND INSIGHTS

Revelations or "light bulb" moments can often be seen as clients make connections that may have been blocked for months or years. Important insights or unexpected links may occur. Giving the client permission and a safe place to release old feelings can help lay the past to rest. Processing continues after the desensitization session and, as clients report a range of experiences, it is important that they are prepared for this and helped with the management of any unexpected reactions.

> It also brought up memories of my younger sister dying, only a year after my operation, which also helped me understand that somehow I felt guilty for feeling angry that she had died, not given me enough time to deal with my own situation before coming to terms with her untimely death. Yes, I cried and cried and cried. I was able to feel the grief and the guilt of not grieving "properly" for my mum and sister.
>
> It was also a way of putting things into perspective and spring cleaning my mind.
>
> And then I remembered when I was a little girl and we lived in a huge Victorian house. It had been a difficult time in my life, and I had generally felt alone and powerless. One of my chores was to go into the cellar and fill the coal bucket. It was cold and scary down there and I often had nightmares, even now, about going down those stone steps. During this part of the eye movements, I could feel that old dread like I was back there. And of course that's where I had first become scared of those big scary creatures! I'd associated the feelings in my life then with the spiders, probably because it would have been too hard as a child to confront the real cause. I don't think I'd ever have made that connection myself so EMDR really helped there.

MOVING FORWARD

As therapists, witnessing clients moving through the pain to a more adaptive future can be an amazing, emotional experience. Sometimes clients need to take time to adjust to changes and freedom from old baggage.

> I was also able to forgive myself for that guilt. Further EMDR and counseling sessions really helped me come to terms with all of those issues. I believe that without EMDR, even that very first session there would have still been issues untapped that would still affect me now.
>
> It was painful emotionally, but I feel that was because I had buried many feelings and memories for so many years, almost becoming an automaton. With the EMDR sessions, the tears flowed freely and by my last EMDR session, the best way I can describe how I felt was *free*! It has also helped me remember the lovely times I shared with my mum and sister, instead of burying those memories away with all the hurt and anguish of the past.

THE THERAPEUTIC RELATIONSHIP

At times when novice practitioners are wondering if they're "getting it right" it's worth remembering that the relationship they are offering to the client is fundamentally healing in many ways. Working with core conditions and offering a safe place for confronting traumatic events is important work and, without this, no amount of therapy will help.

> At the time when having treatment I was hurting really bad I just wanted to give up (I thought). What I wanted her to do was to give up on me. She never did and I'm glad now.
>
> The most important thing was to treat me with respect and be amazingly supportive—both things I had never really experienced in my life. Also her confidence in EMDR supported me through difficult times.

THE OUTCOME OF EMDR

If ever the learning curve gets too steep, and despondency sets in, stop and read some inspirational stories. Keep a file with your letters and cards of thanks.

> It has helped me beyond measure. I now realize what I was dealing with for the whole of my life and the times when I thought I must be weak or pathetic I was actually courageous and strong. I just didn't realize it and neither did anyone else.
>
> Thankfully, I was truly blessed to have EMDR, which broke my emotional stalemate, got me in touch with what had really gone on in my past and how it really was affecting me. It touched me deeply. It reached deep inside, where no other therapy had. I am forever thankful that I was given the opportunity to experience those powerful yet painful visits to my past....and lucky I had a wonderful therapist who knew that was exactly what I needed.
>
> EMDR helped me by making me put things into perspective, I got rid of a lot of garbage from my past, and it made me realize it wasn't my fault; it was nobody's. It also made me see how much I don't relax, and how I think of things over and over again, my mind never rests.
>
> I would describe it as a spring cleaning of the mind. If I imagine my mind as a huge filing cabinet, EMDR makes you open the drawers one by one, deal with issues by looking at them from a different perspective, helps you to get rid of all the old stuff leaving you with clean organized drawers.

The best form of recommendation for anything is that which comes from someone who has been there. The final words come from clients who have experienced EMDR. What would they tell others who are considering this psychotherapy?

> If I knew someone who was considering EMDR, I would tell them that it is like having "A foot in the past and a foot in the present." It can be emotionally painful, but I do believe it is the most powerful way I can imagine that can exorcise demons from the past. It gives you a chance to really rid yourself of anguish and pain from your trauma.
>
> Feel the fear and do it anyway! The fear you feel will not be the fear that you felt at the time of your trauma....it is a remembered fear and it will help you put your present fears into perspective. Most importantly, it will help you move forward in your life.
>
> If I knew someone who was considering EMDR I would say to him or her "why are you not having the treatment now?" Then I would pass them the phone, dial the number, and say "do it!"

Appendix E: Glossary of Terms and Acronyms

Abreaction	A high level of distress that a client experiences as they reprocess a memory.
Adaptive information processing (AIP) theory	AIP theory posits that EMDR involves the forging of associations between the dysfunctional stored material and more adaptive memory networks.
Alters	Identity states that recurrently take executive control of an individual's behavior—a specific symptom of DID.
Assessment	The third phase of the EMDR protocol during which the components of the target memory are elicited thus establishing the baseline measures to determine the client's response to desensitisation and to activate the memory that the client will be reprocessing.
Blocked processing	Processing can be said to be blocked when the client has not desensitised the target memory or installed the PC to a fitting level, reprocessing has stopped and no changes are reported after two consecutive sets.
Body scan	The body scan is the sixth phase of the EMDR protocol. The therapist will assess adaptive resolution of the target by asking the client to hold the original memory, whilst considering the positive cognition, and checking their body for any tension or sensation. The therapist should then target any residual physical manifestation with DAS.
Case conceptualisation	See Three-pronged approach.
Channels of association	Channels refer to associated thoughts, images, emotions, memories and physical sensations that are somehow connected in the memory network.

Closure	Closure is the seventh phase of the EMDR protocol. During this phase (if the session is incomplete) the client's emotional state is stabilized. They are fully debriefed and advised to keep a log.
Clustering	Clusters are groups of memory that share some common aspect, e.g. NC, setting or type of traumatic incident. By choosing a representative memory from a cluster, EMDR may facilitate a generalisation effect across the cluster of memories. This generalisation is often referred to as the domino effect meaning that other memories in that cluster lose their emotional resonance.
Cognitive interweaves	The cognitive interweave aims to help the client make the connections they are not making spontaneously. The therapist offers statements that will help the client access positive memory networks and interweave that material into the traumatic material during desensitization.
Cues	Internal or external cues may stimulate stored information. They may be targeted for desensitization as part of the treatment plan.
DAS	DAS is the Dual Attention Stimulation used in Desensitisation, Installation and Body Scan and may be in the form of sets of eye movements, audio or tactile stimulus. A set is the continuous application of DAS and each set is interspersed by the request for brief client feedback.
DDNOS	Dissociative Disorders Not Otherwise Specified
DES	Dissociative Experiences Scale
DES-T	Dissociative Experiences Scale—Taxon
Desensitization	Desensitization is the fourth phase of the EMDR protocol. The effect of desensitization is to reduce the disturbance related to the target memory and associated cues. SUDS are used to measure the treatment effect.
Desired state	The desired state is expressed initially as the Positive Cognition and reflects how the client wishes to think, feel and behave in the future.
DSM IV	Diagnostic Statistician Manual 4th edition published by the American Psychiatric Association
Dysfunctional information	Dysfunctional information includes disturbing thoughts, feelings, sensations and behavior that can be triggered by external or internal cues. These cues may relate to unresolved, past experiences.

Ecological validity	Ecological validity needs to be considered where, despite having made the appropriate efforts to continue processing, the SUDS are still greater than 0 or 1. The appropriateness of a residual level of emotional disturbance is determined by the individual's unique situation and should be considered in this wider context.
Feeder memories	Feeder memories are earlier memories that can sometimes block the processing of later incidents. Our earliest assumptions and representations generally have a far greater impact on our conceptual system than that which comes later. Feeder memories are not always easily apparent and will need to be identified and reprocessed.
Generalisation effect	See Clustering
History taking	History Taking is the first phase of the EMDR protocol. Information is gathered in order to ascertain client appropriateness for EMDR treatment. This will include taking the client's history, determining the current level of functioning along with goals for therapy, safety factors and selection of targets for processing.
Incomplete sessions	An incomplete session is where the processing is not complete and SUDS remain above 0 or 1 The client is left with residual emotional disturbance that needs to be stabilized. See Closure.
Installation	Installation is the fifth phase of the EMDR protocol. The Installation phase is concerned with integrating the positive cognition with the targeted memory. This would only be done after desensitization is complete.
Journal or Log	The journal, or log, is a written record of material that arises between sessions. It can include significant thoughts, emotions, behaviors and dreams and will help guide re-evaluation and treatment planning.
Looping	Looping is said to occur when a client is reporting the same or basically similar images, thoughts, emotions or sensations in consecutive sets. Affect remains the same and no new insights are being made. It is a form of blocked processing.
NC	Negative Cognition
NICE	National Institute of Clinical Excellence

Nodes	The target for processing can be considered as a node. The node will have channels where associated thoughts, images, emotions, memories and physical sensations are stored.
PC	Positive Cognition
Preparation	Preparation is the second phase of the EMDR protocol. In this phase, the therapeutic relationship is being built and a clear explanation of EMDR given. Client fears and expectations are addressed, a safe place is established and eye movements or other form of DAS are tested.
Prioritising	The selection of those targets to be processed first as part of the three-pronged approach.
Re-evaluation	Re-evaluation is the eighth phase of EMDR. Re-evaluation is done at the beginning of each session following a desensitisaion session. It involves reviewing the client's journal, assessing the current state of the previously targeted material, considering the subsequent targets and treatment plan.
Safe place	The safe place is an imagery location that can be used to stabilize the client, during, after and between sessions. It can be a valuable self-help tool.
Situationally accessible memory	The SAM is the situationally accessible memory that is composed largely of nonverbal data received during the occurrence of some kind of traumatic event.
Sets	See DAS
SMART	A useful acronym for goal setting—Specific, Measurable, Achievable, Realistic and Time-framed
State changes	State changes are changes in the presenting symptoms leading to temporary relief, whilst not necessarily resolving the underlying factors by making trait changes.
SUDS	Subjective Units of Disturbance Scale
Targets	See Nodes
Three-pronged approach	The three-pronged approach identifies specific targets for reprocessing—past, present and future. These are the past memories that appeared to have set the pathology in process, the present situations that exacerbate this dysfunction and the desired future response.

Touchstone event	Memories and associated beliefs are built on each other over a lifetime. A touchstone event is the earliest occurrence of a particular cognitive schema or affective response linked to the current pathology.
Trait changes	See State changes
Treatment plan	See Three-pronged approach
Triggers	See Cues
Verbally Accessible Memory	The verbally accessible memory is where memories are stored in an accessible form and can be retrieved as and when required.
VOC	Validity of cognition self-report scale

References

Adams Betts, K., Matto, H., & Harrington, D. (2001). The Traumatic Stress Institute Belief Scale as a measure of vicarious trauma in a national sample of clinical social workers. *Families in Society: The Journal of Contemporary Human Services, 82,* 363–371.

American Psychiatric Association. (1994). *Diagnostic and statistical manual of mental disorders* (4th ed.). Washington, DC: Author.

Andrade, J., Kavanagh, D., & Baddeley, A. (1997). Eye-movement and visual imagery: A working memory approach to the treatment of post-traumatic stress disorder. *British Journal of Clinical Psychology, 36,* 209–223.

Benson, H. (2000). *The relaxation response.* New York: Harper Collins.

Bernstein, C., & Putnam, F. W. (1986). Development, reliability and validity of a dissociation scale. *Journal of Nervous and Mental Diseases, 174,* 727–735.

Blake, D.D., Weather, F.W., Nagy, L.M., Kaloupek, D.G., Gusman, F.D., Cherney, D.S. & Keane, T.M. (1995) The development of a clinician-administered PTSD scale. *Journal of Traumatic Stress, 8,* 75–90

Bourne, I., & Oliver, B. (1999). *Course notes: Diploma in posttraumatic stress counselling.* London: The Richmond Fellowship.

Bowlby, J. (1980). *Attachment and loss.* New York: Basic Books.

Brewin, C. R. (2003). *Post-traumatic stress disorder: Malady or myth?* New Haven, CT: Yale University Press.

Bride, B., Robinson, M., Yegidis, B., & Figley, C. (2003). Development and validation of the secondary traumatic stress scale. *Research on Social Work Practice, 13,* 1–16.

Briere, J. (2002). *Multiscale Dissociation Inventory.* Odessa, FL: Psychological Assessment Resources.

Briere, J., & Spinazzola, J. (2005). Phenomenology and psychological assessment of complex posttraumatic states. *Journal of Traumatic Stress, 18*(5), 401–412.

Brown, K. W., McGoldrick, T., & Buchanan, R. (1997). Body dysmorphic disorder: Seven cases treated with eye movement desensitisation and reprocessing. *Behavioural and Cognitive Psychotherapy, 25*(2), 203–207.

Carlson, J. G., Chemtob, C. M., Rusnac, K., Hedlund, N. L., & Muraoka, M. Y. (1998). Eye movement desensitisation and reprocessing for combat related post traumatic stress disorder. *Journal of Traumatic Stress, 11,* 3–24.

Chemtob, C. M., Tolin, D. F., van der Kolk, B. A., & Pitman, R. K. (2000). Eye movement desensitisation and reprocessing. In E. B. Foa, T. M. Kean, & M. J. Friedman (Eds.), *Effective treatments for PTSD: Practice guidelines from the International Society for Traumatic Stress Studies.* New York: Guilford Press, 139–154

Clinical Resource Efficiency Support Team (CREST). (2003). *The management of post traumatic stress disorder in adults.* Belfast, Northern Ireland: Department of Health.

Dell, P. F., & O'Neill, J. A. (2009). *Dissociation and the dissociative disorders: DSM-V and beyond.* Oxford, England: Routledge.

Demerouti, E., Bakker, A., Vardakou, I., & Kantas, A. (2003). The convergent validity of two burnout instruments: A multitrait-multimethod analysis. *European Journal of Psychological Assessment, 19*, 12–23.

Department of Veterans Affairs & Department of Defence. (2004). *VA/DoD clinical practice guidelines for the management of post traumatic stress.* Washington, DC: Author.

DePrince, A. P., & Cromer, L. D. (2006). *Exploring dissociation: Definitions, development and cognitive correlates.* New York: Haworth Medical Press.

DePrince, A. P., & Freyd, J. J. (2007). Trauma-induced dissociation. In M. J. Friedman, T. M. Keane, & P. A. Resick (Eds.), *Handbook of PTSD: Science and practice* (pp. 135–150). New York: Guilford Press.

Dyregrov, A., Solomon, R., & Bassoe, C. F. (2000). Mental mobilisation processes in critical incident stress situations. *International Journal of Emergency Mental Health, 2*(2), 73–81.

Figley, C. (Ed.). (1995). *Compassion fatigue: Coping with secondary traumatic stress disorder in those who treat the traumatised.* New York: Brunner/Mazel.

First, M. B., Spitzer, R. L., Gibbon, M., & Williams, J. B. W (1997). *Structured Clinical Interview for DSM IV Axis 1 Disorders—Clinician Version (SCID—CV).* Washington, DC: American Psychiatric Press.

Forgash, C., & Copeley, M. (Eds.). (2008). *Healing the heart of trauma and dissociation with EMDR and ego state therapy.* New York: Springer.

Herman, J. L. (1992). *Trauma and recovery.* New York: Basic Books.

Ironson, G. L., Freund, B., Stauss, J. L., & Williams, J. (2002). Comparison of two treatments for traumatic stress: A community based study of EMDR and prolonged exposure. *Journal of Clinical Psychology, 58*, 113–128.

Janoff-Bulman, R. (1985). *Shattered assumptions, towards a new psychology of trauma.* New York: The Free Press.

Karjala, L. M. (2007). *Understanding trauma and dissociation: A guide for therapists, patients and loved ones.* Atlanta, GA: Thomas Max.

Kavanaugh, D. J., Freese, S., Andrade, J., & May, J. (2001). Effects of visuospatial tasks on desensitization to emotive memories. *British Journal of Clinical Psychology, 40*, 267–280.

Keenan, P., & Royle, E. (2008). Vicarious trauma and first responders: A case study utilising Eye Movement Desensitisation and Reprocessing (EMDR) as the primary treatment modality. *International Journal of Emergency Mental Health, 9*(4), 291–298.

Keenan, P. S., & Farrell, D. P. (2000). Treating non-psychotic morbid jealousy with EMDR, utilising cognitive interweave: A case report. *Counselling Psychology Quarterly, 13*(2), 175–189.

Kiessling, R. (2005). Integrating resource development strategies into your EMDR practice. In R. Shapiro (Ed.), *EMDR solutions: Pathways to healing.* New York: Norton, 57–87.

Kluft, R. P., Steinberg, M., & Spitzer, R. L. (1988). DSM III revisions in the dissociative disorders: An exploration of the derivation and rationale. *Dissociation, 1*, 39–46.

Leeds, A. M. (2009). Resources in EMDR and other trauma-focused psychotherapy: A review. *Journal of EMDR Practice and Research, 3*(3), 152–160.

Loewenstein, R. J. (1991). An office mental status examination for complex chronic dissociative symptoms and multiple personality disorder. *Psychiatric Clinics of North America, 14*(3), 567–604.

Maslach, C., Jackson, S., & Leiter, M.P. (1996). *MBI: The Maslach Burnout Inventory: Manual* Palo Alto, CA: Consulting Psychologists Press.

Maxfield, L. & Hyer, L. (2002) The relationship between efficacy and methodology in studies investigating EMDR treatment of PTSD. *Journal of Clinical Psychology, 58*(1), 139–154.

McCann, L. I., & Pearlman, L. A. (1990). Vicarious traumatisation: A framework for understanding the psychological effects of working with victims. *Journal of Traumatic Stress, 3*, 131–149.

Moskowitz, A., Schafer, I., & Dorahy, M. J. (2008). *Psychosis, trauma and dissociation: Emerging perspectives on severe psychopathology.* West Sussex, England: Wiley-Blackwell.

Muss, D. (1991). *The trauma trap.* London: Doubleday.

National Institute for Clinical Excellence (NICE). (2005). *The management of post traumatic stress disorder (PTSD) in adults and children in primary and secondary care.* London: Author.

Nijenhuis, E. R. (1999). *Somatoform dissociation: Phenomena, measurement and theoretical issues.* Assen, The Netherlands: Van Gorcum.

Ogden, P., Minton, K., & Pain, C. (2006). *Trauma and the body: A sensorimotor approach to psychotherapy.* New York: Norton.

Parnell, L. (2007). *A therapist's guide to EMDR: Tools and techniques for successful treatment.* New York: Norton.

Pearlman, L., & Saakvitne, K. (1995). *Trauma and the therapist: Countertransference and vicarious traumatization in psychotherapy with incest survivors.* New York: Norton.

Philips, G., & Buncher, L. (1999). *Gold counselling: A structured psychotherapeutic approach to the mapping and re-aligning of belief systems* (2nd ed.). Carmarthen, Wales: Crown House.

Pines, A., & Aronson, E. (1988). *Career burnout: Causes and cures* (2nd ed.). New York: Free Press.

Potter, B. (1998). *Overcoming job burnout: How to renew enthusiasm for work.* Berkeley, CA: Ronin.

Power, K. G., McGoldrick, T., Brown, K., Buchanan, R., Sharp, D., & Swanson, V. (2002). A controlled comparison of eye movement desensitisation and reprocessing, versus exposure plus cognitive restructuring, versus, waiting list in the treatment of post traumatic stress disorder. *Journal of Clinical Psychology and psychotherapy, 9*, 299–318.

Rogers, C. (1995). *A way of being* (2nd ed.). Boston: Houghton Mifflin.

Ross, C. A. (1989). *Multiple personality disorder: Diagnosis, clinical features and treatment.* West Sussex, England: Wiley.

Ross, C. A. (1996). *Dissociative identity disorder: Diagnosis, clinical features and treatment* (2nd ed.). West Sussex, England: Wiley.

Ross, C. A., Anderson, G., Fraser, G. A., Reagor, P., Bjornson, L., & Miller, S. D. (1992). Differentiating multiple personality disorder and dissociative disorder not otherwise specified. *Dissociation, 5,* 88–91.

Ross, C. A., Herber, S., Norton, G. R., & Anderson, G. (1989). Differences between multiple personality disorder and other diagnostic groups on structured interview. *Journal of Nervous Mental Disease, 177,* 487–491.

Rothschild, B. (2000). *The body remembers: The psychophysiology of trauma and trauma treatment.* New York: Norton.

Rothschild, B. (2006). *Help for the helper: The psychophysiology of compassion fatigue and vicarious trauma.* New York: Norton.

Royle, E. (2008). Eye Movement Desensitization and Reprocessing (EMDR) in the treatment of chronic fatigue syndrome. *Journal of EMDR Practice and Research, 2*(3), 226–232.

Schore, A. (1996). The experience-dependent maturation of a regulatory system in the orbital pre-frontal cortex and the origin of developmental psychopathology. *Development and Psychopathology, 8,* 59–87.

Scott, M. J. (2008). *Moving on after trauma: A guide for survivors, family and friends.* London: Routledge.

Scott, M. J., & Stradling, S. G. (2001). *Counselling for post traumatic stress disorder* (2nd ed.). London: Sage.

Shapiro, F. (2001). *Eye movement desensitization and reprocessing: Basic principles, protocols and procedures* (2nd ed.). New York: Guilford Press.

Shapiro, R. (2005). *Solutions: Pathways to healing.* New York: Norton.

Sharpley, C. F., Montgomery, I. M., & Scalzo, L. A. (1996). Comparative efficacy of EMDR and alternative procedures in reducing the vividness of mental images. *Scandinavian Journal of Behaviour Therapy, 25,* 37–42.

Soberman, G. B., Greenwald, R., & Rule, D. L. (2002). A controlled study of eye movement desensitisation and reprocessing (EMDR) for boys with conduct problems. *Journal of Aggression, Maltreatment and Trauma, 6,* 217–236.

Stamm, B. (2002). Measuring compassion satisfaction as well as fatigue: Developmental history of the compassion satisfaction and fatigue test. In C. Figley (Ed.), *Treating compassion fatigue* (pp. 107–118). Philadelphia: Brunner-Routledge.

Steinberg, M. (1995). *Handbook for the assessment of dissociation: A clinical guide.* Washington, DC: American Psychiatric Press.

Terr, L. (1994). *Unchained memories.* New York: Basic.

Thomas, K. (1995). The defensive self: A psychodynamic perspective. In R. Stevens (Ed.), *Understanding the self.* London: Sage, 281–338.

Tinker, R. H., & Wilson, S. A. (2005).The phantom limb pain protocol. In R. Shapiro (Ed.), *EMDR solutions: Pathways to healing.* New York: Norton, 147–159.

Valent, P. (1995). Survival strategies: A framework for understanding secondary traumatic stress and coping in helpers. In C. R. Figley (Ed.), *Compassion fatigue: Coping with secondary traumatic stress disorder in those who treat the traumatised.* New York: Brunner/Mazel, 21–50.

Van den Hout, M., Muris, P., Salemink, E., & Kindt, M. (2001). Autobiographical memories become less vivid and emotional after eye movements. *British Journal of Clinical Psychology, 40,* 121–130.

Van der Kolk, B. (2006). Clinical implications of neuroscience research in PTSD. *Annals of the New York Academy of Sciences, 1–17.*

Van der Kolk, B. A., McFarlane, A. C., & Weisaeth, L. (Eds.). (1996). *Traumatic stress: The effects of overwhelming experience on mind, body and society*. New York: Guilford Press.

Waller, N. G., Putnam, F. W., & Carlson, E. B. (1996). Types of dissociation and dissociative types: A taxometric analysis of dissociative experiences. *Psychological Methods, 1*, 300–321.

Watkins, J. G. (1997). *Ego states: Theory and therapy*. New York: Norton.

Weiss, D. S., & Marmar, C. R. (1996). The impact of event scale—revised. In J. Wilson & T. M. Keane (Eds.), *Assessing psychological trauma and PTSD*. New York: Guilford Press, 399–411.

Young, J. E. (1990). *Cognitive therapy for personality disorder: A schema focussed approach*. Sarsota, FL: Professional Resource Exchange.

Index

CPSIA information can be obtained at www.ICGtesting.com
Printed in the USA
BVOW01s2141170816

459245BV00008B/17/P